DIRECT CURRENT GEOELECTRIC SOUNDING

SERIES

Methods in Geochemistry and Geophysics

Methods in Geochemistry and Geophysics

9

DIRECT CURRENT GEOELECTRIC SOUNDING

PRINCIPLES AND INTERPRETATION

BY

P. K. BHATTACHARYA AND H. P. PATRA

Department of Geology and Geophysics,
Indian Institute of Technology,
Kharagpur, West Bengal, India

ELSEVIER PUBLISHING COMPANY
AMSTERDAM / LONDON / NEW YORK
1968

ELSEVIER PUBLISHING COMPANY
335 JAN VAN GALENSTRAAT
P. O. BOX 211, AMSTERDAM, THE NETHERLANDS

ELSEVIER PUBLISHING COMPANY LTD.
BARKING, ESSEX, ENGLAND

AMERICAN ELSEVIER PUBLISHING COMPANY, INC.
52 VANDERBILT AVENUE
NEW YORK, NEW YORK 10017

LIBRARY OF CONGRESS CATALOG CARD NUMBER 68-15628

WITH 47 ILLUSTRATIONS AND 16 TABLES

PRINTED IN THE NETHERLANDS

Preface

The present volume is based on lectures, laboratory exercises, and field problems on geoelectric sounding which were organised for senior students in exploration geophysics at the Indian Institute of Technology, Kharagpur, West Bengal (India). It may therefore be used as a textbook on geoelectric sounding (as part of a course on electrical methods of prospecting) on the undergraduate or post-graduate level.

The need for a comprehensive book on this subject has long been felt by geologists and geophysicists engaged in resistivity sounding for mining and engineering geological problems. The publication of three- and four-layer theoretical master curves for Wenner arrangement (MOONEY and WETZEL) in 1956 by the University of Minnesota, of an album of three-layer theoretical master curves for Schlumberger arrangement (COMPAGNIE GÉNÉRALE DE GÉOPHYSIQUE) in 1955 (reissued in a more organised and modified form in 1963) by the European Association of Exploration Geophysicists and recently (1966) of an album of charts by ORELLANA and MOONEY, has considerably increased the necessity for such a book on the subject. The aim of this work is to give students in exploration geophysics a comprehensive idea and elaborate techniques of interpretation of Schlumberger, Wenner and dipole sounding curves, with a reasonable accuracy, together with an adequate number of plates and charts for the purpose. Attempts have been made to explain, in brief, the various field layouts together with plans for the same. A sufficient number of examples with carefully drawn self-explanatory diagrams have been presented which are followed by problems at the end of the chapters to serve as exercises for the students. However, no attempt has been made to include instrumentation or any detailed description of measurement techniques.

Although the book is primarily meant for students, it can be profitably used by professional exploration geologists and geophysicists engaged in resistivity sounding for exploration of minerals, ground water, bed rock depth, and structural features for oil.

Civil engineers, particularly those interested in the determination of quality and depth of bed rock, will find this book a self-sufficient and useful aid in their profession. Agricultural scientists and engineers interested in the exploration of ground water for irrigation and other projects may also find this book of value.

It is a pleasure to thank Dr. T. C. Bagchi, Head of the Department of Geology and Geophysics and other colleagues for facilities and encouragement offered in preparing this book. The assistance offered by Sri N. G. Sarkar in preparing the charts and drawings is appreciated. Discussions with some of our advanced students have been useful, and we are thankful to them. The Director, Indian Institute of Technology, Kharagpur, has kindly permitted publication of this book outside the institute.

We shall appreciate receiving comments and suggestions for improving the value and utility of this work.

Kharagpur (India)   P. K. BHATTACHARYA and H. P. PATRA

Contents

Enclosure loose Plates I–X

CONTENTS

CHAPTER 1

Introduction

Geoelectricity is a member of a group of sciences known as the geophysical sciences. It deals with the electrical state of the earth and includes discussions on the electrical properties of rocks and minerals under different geological environments, as well as their influences upon various geophysical phenomena. Geoelectric exploration (or, more simply, electrical exploration) is a major branch of exploration geophysics. It uses the principles of geoelectricity for geological mapping of concealed structures, for the exploration and prospecting of ores, minerals, and oil, and in the solution of many hydrogeological and engineering geological problems.

It was formerly believed that geoelectric methods were suitable only for shallow exploration, and such methods were therefore primarily used for mining and engineering geophysical problems. Today, however, modern developments and refined techniques of interpretation have considerably increased the depth of investigation. It is now claimed (particularly by Soviet geophysicists) that exploration by geoelectric methods may be carried out with reasonable accuracy down to depths of 8–10 km.

Geoelectric exploration consists of exceedingly diverse principles and techniques, and utilizes both stationary and variable currents produced either artificially or by natural processes. One of the most widely used methods of geoelectric exploration is known as the resistivity method. In this, a current (a direct or very low frequency alternating current) is introduced into the ground by two or more electrodes, and the potential difference is measured between two points (probes) suitably chosen with respect to the current electrodes. The potential difference for unit current sent through the ground is a measure of the electrical resistance of the ground between the probes. The resistance is a function of the geometrical configuration of the electrodes and the electrical parameters of the ground. Broadly speaking, we can distinguish two types of resistivity measurements. In the first, known as geoelectric profiling or mapping, the electrodes and probes are shifted without changing their relative configurations. This gives us an idea of the surface variation of resistance values within a certain depth. In the second method, known as geoelectric sounding, the positions of the electrodes are changed with respect to a fixed point (known as the sounding point). In this way, the measured resistance values at the surface reflect the vertical distribution of resistivity values in a geological section. In this book we are primarily concerned with resistivity sounding only.

The two types of electrode configurations which are most frequently used in resistivity sounding are called the Wenner and Schlumberger arrays. While the Wenner configuration is used in the United States and Canada, and in other English-speaking countries, the Schlumberger configuration is almost exclusively used in European countries and in the U.S.S.R.

Descriptions of the Wenner method of sounding, and the techniques for its interpretation, are available in a number of textbooks written in the English language. On the other hand, descriptions of the Schlumberger method of sounding, and of the powerful techniques of interpretation which have developed chiefly outside the English-speaking world (notably by French and Soviet geophysicists), are mentioned in only a few English textbooks. The main purpose of this book, therefore, is to bring to English-speaking students, research workers, and practicing geophysicists a detailed description of the Schlumberger method of geoelectric sounding as well as of techniques of interpretation which are available at present.

The main text is divided into five chapters, which are briefly described below:

Chapter 2 deals with the theoretical foundations of geoelectric sounding, since a sound understanding of basic principles is essential for students specializing in the field. This chapter helps to create a solid background for what will be discussed in subsequent chapters. A reader lacking the mathematical background necessary for a grasp of these concepts may skip over this chapter and still follow without difficulty the interpretation techniques explained in subsequent chapters.

Chapter 3, giving a detailed description of the Schlumberger method of sounding, forms the major portion of this book. The interpretation of field curves has been facilitated by the recent publication of three- and four-layer theoretical master curves. Since these curves do not represent all the field conditions that are met in practice, a rapid and reasonably accurate method of constructing master curves by graphical and semi-analytical means is included. The chapter also includes a somewhat detailed description of the interpretation of Schlumberger curves with figures presented in this book. These may be used in conjunction with the theoretical master curves available in published form. However, the procedure for interpreting Schlumberger curves with the help of charts given in this volume comes only at the expense of some loss in accuracy. It should be mentioned here that the master curves mentioned above are plotted on double-logarithm graph paper with a modulus of 62.5 mm. This paper is sometimes difficult to obtain in English-speaking countries, although it is easily available in countries where the metric system is used. If this paper is not readily available, students may use transparent double-logarithm graph sheets with a modulus of $2\frac{1}{3}$ inches, without risking any serious error in interpretation.

Chapter 4 explains, in brief, the relative merits and drawbacks of the two symmetrical arrangements for vertical electrical sounding, followed by methods of interpretation available for Wenner sounding curves.

Chapter 5 gives a short description of dipole sounding, a modern development in deep electrical sounding. This method is widely used in the Soviet Union for mapping basement structures.

Chapter 6 discusses the various fields of application of geoelectric sounding.

The principles dealt with in each chapter have been illustrated by means of a sufficient number of typical, worked-out examples given at the end of each chapter. Some problems have also been included.

This volume, together with the albums of curves by the COMPAGNIE GÉNÉRALE DE GÉOPHYSIQUE (1955, 1963), ANONYMOUS (1957, 1963a, b, c) and MOONEY and WETZEL (1956) makes a complete unit for class, laboratory and field use in resistivity sounding with Schlumberger, Wenner and dipole arrays.

CHAPTER 2

Theoretical Foundations

This chapter deals with the theory of current flow in a horizontally stratified earth. A proper understanding of the theory is necessary for the appreciation of various interpretation techniques dealt with in later chapters. Some basic concepts regarding anisotropy and apparent resistivity are introduced, and principles of vertical and dipole electrical resistivity sounding are explained.

CURRENT FLOW IN A HOMOGENEOUS EARTH

The flow of current in a medium is based on the *principle of conservation of charge* and is expressed by the relation:

$$\operatorname{div} \bar{J} = -\frac{\partial q}{\partial t} \tag{2.1}$$

where $\bar{J}$ is the current density (A/m^2) and q is the charge density (C/m^n). This relation (2.1) is also known as the "equation of continuity". For stationary current (2.1) reduces to:

$$\operatorname{div} \bar{J} = 0 \tag{2.2}$$

If ρ is the resistivity (Ωm) of the medium, then the current density $\bar{J}$ is related to the electric field intensity $\bar{E}$ (V/m) by means of Ohm's law, which is given as:

$$\bar{J} = \frac{1}{\rho} \bar{E} = -\frac{1}{\rho} \operatorname{grad} V \tag{2.3}$$

where V is the electric potential (volts). For an isotropic medium, ρ is a scalar function of the point of observation, and $\bar{J}$ is in the same direction as $\bar{E}$. In an anisotropic medium, however, $\bar{J}$ has a directive property and, in general, is not in the direction of $\bar{E}$. This requires some modification in Ohm's law.

For a rectangular coordinate system we can write the modified Ohm's law as:

$$
\begin{aligned}
J_x &= \sigma_{xx}E_x + \sigma_{xy}E_y + \sigma_{xz}E_z \\
J_y &= \sigma_{yx}E_x + \sigma_{yy}E_y + \sigma_{yz}E_z \\
J_z &= \sigma_{zx}E_x + \sigma_{zy}E_y + \sigma_{zz}E_z
\end{aligned} \quad\quad (2.4)
$$

where σ_{ik} may be defined as the electric field in the direction of k when a unit current density is in the direction of i. It can be shown from conservation principle that $\sigma_{ik} = \sigma_{ki}$. Thus, in an anisotropic medium conductivity is a symmetric tensor having six components. The current flow in an anisotropic medium will be treated later.

For an isotropic medium we get from relations (2.2) and (2.3):

$$
\text{div}\left(\frac{1}{\rho} \text{ grad } V\right) = 0 \quad\quad (2.5)
$$

or:

$$
\text{grad}\left(\frac{1}{\rho}\right) \cdot \text{grad } V + \frac{1}{\rho} \text{ div grad } V = 0 \quad\quad (2.6)
$$

This is the fundamental equation of electrical prospecting with direct current. If the medium is homogeneous, ρ is independent of the coordinate axes and eq.(2.6) reduces to: div grad $V = 0$, or:

$$
\nabla^2 V = 0 \quad\quad (2.7)
$$

Thus, the electric potential distribution for direct current flow in a homogeneous isotropic medium satisfies Laplace's equation.

Let us now suppose that a current I be introduced into an infinite homogeneous medium at a point P. Then the potential at a distance r from P will be only a function of r. Hence Laplace's equation can be written as:

$$
\frac{d^2V}{dr^2} + \frac{2}{r} \frac{dV}{dr} = 0
$$

a solution of which is:

$$V = C_1 + \frac{C_2}{r} \qquad (2.8)$$

As the potential is taken to be zero at a large distance from the source, the integration constant $C_1 = 0$. It is clear that the equipotential surfaces are spherical, and the electric field lines as well as the current lines are radial. The current density at a distance r may be written as:

$$J = -\frac{1}{\rho} \frac{\partial V}{\partial r} = \frac{1}{\rho} \frac{C_2}{r^2}$$

Thus, the total current flowing out of a spherical surface of radius r is:

$$4\pi r^2 J = \frac{4\pi}{\rho} C_2$$

Since this is equal to I, the total current introduced at P, the constant C_2 is given by: $C_2 = I\rho/4\pi$.

For a semi-infinite medium, i.e., when the current is introduced into a homogeneous ground, the total current flowing out of a hemispherical surface of radius r is given by the relation, $2\pi r^2 J = (2\pi/\rho)C_2$, and the constant C_2 is equal to $I\rho/2\pi$.

Thus, the potential at any point due to a current source at the surface of a homogeneous earth is:

$$V = \frac{I\rho}{2\pi} \frac{1}{r} \qquad (2.9)$$

In practice, the current is introduced into the ground by means of two electrodes, i.e., a source and a sink; and the potential at any point due to this "bipolar" arrangement is:

$$V = \frac{I\rho}{2\pi} \left(\frac{1}{r_1} - \frac{1}{r_2} \right) \qquad (2.10)$$

where r_1 and r_2 are the distances of the point P from the source and the sink, respectively.

RESISTIVITY MEASUREMENT

Consider that a direct current of strength I is introduced into a homogeneous and isotropic earth by means of two point electrodes A and B (Fig.1). The potential difference between the two points M and N on the surface is given by—using eq.(2.10):

$$V = \frac{I\rho}{2\pi} \left\{ \left(\frac{1}{AM} - \frac{1}{BM} \right) - \left(\frac{1}{AN} - \frac{1}{BN} \right) \right\} \quad (2.11)$$

where ρ is the resistivity of the ground. Thus, the resistivity of the homogeneous earth can be determined from the measurements on the surface.

Various electrode arrangements for A, B, M, and N have been suggested for the purpose. The ones more commonly used for re-

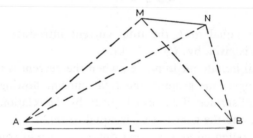

Fig.1. Point electrodes over a homogeneous and isotropic earth. A, B = point source and sink; M, N = observation points on the surface of the earth.

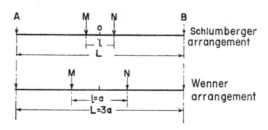

Fig.2. Symmetrical electrode arrangements. Top: Schlumberger arrangement ($AB = L$, $MN = l$; $l \leqslant L/5$). Bottom: Wenner arrangement ($l = a$, $L = 3a$; $l = L/3$).

sistivity sounding are: (*I*) symmetrical arrangement, and (*2*) dipole arrangement.

In the symmetrical arrangement, the points A, M, N, B are taken on a straight line such that the points M and N are symmetrically placed about the centre O of the "spread" AB (Fig.2).

Here:

$$\Delta V = \frac{I\rho}{2\pi} \left(\frac{4}{L-l} - \frac{4}{L+l} \right) \tag{2.12}$$

which gives:

$$\rho = \frac{\pi}{4} \frac{(L^2 - l^2)}{l} \frac{\Delta V}{I} \tag{2.13}$$

In the *Wenner arrangement*, L is taken equal to $3l$ (l is conventionally denoted by "a" in the Wenner configuration and is known as spacing or separation of the electrodes), and the resistivity is given by:

$$\rho = 2\pi a \frac{\Delta V}{I} \tag{2.14}$$

If $L \geqslant 5l$, we can put $(L^2 - l^2)$ in eq.(2.13) equal to L^2 with an error less than 4%. This is known as the *Schlumberger arrangement* (Fig.2). In this case, the resistivity is given by:

$$\rho = \frac{\pi L^2}{4} \frac{\Delta V}{l} \frac{1}{I} = \frac{\pi L^2}{4} \frac{E}{I} \tag{2.15}$$

where $E = \Delta V/l$ is (approximately) the electric intensity at the central point O. Hence, this arrangement is sometimes known as the "gradient arrangement", and Wenner's arrangement as a "potential arrangement".

The general *dipole arrangement* is shown in Fig.3, where r is usually taken to be much larger than AB. The potential at O due to AB is given by:

$$V = \frac{I\rho}{2\pi} \left(\frac{1}{AO} - \frac{1}{BO} \right)$$

$$= \frac{I\rho}{2\pi r} [\{1 + (L/2r)^2 - (L/r) \cos \theta\}^{-\frac{1}{2}}$$

$$- \{1 + (L/2r)^2 + (L/r) \cos \theta\}^{-\frac{1}{2}}]$$

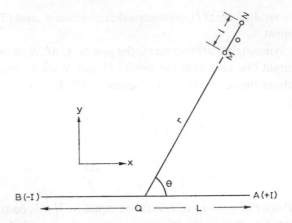

Fig.3. A general arrangement for dipole electrical sounding. AB = current dipole; MN = measuring dipole; Q, O = midpoints of current and measuring dipoles.

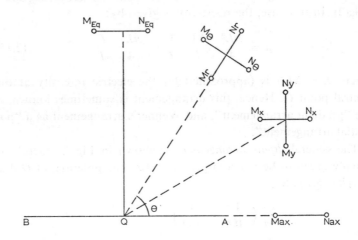

Fig.4. Various arrangements for dipole sounding. $M_{ax}N_{ax}$ = axial; M_xN_x = = parallel; M_yN_y = perpendicular; M_rN_r = radial; $M_\theta N_\theta$ = azimuthal; $M_{eq}N_{eq}$ = equatorial.

which can be expressed in a series, and the potential may be written as:

$$V = \frac{I\rho L \cos \theta}{2\pi r^2} \{1 + (L/2r)^2 \tfrac{1}{2}(5 \cos^2 \theta - 3) + \text{higher-order terms}\}$$
(2.16)

If $r \gg L$, the expression (2.16) may approximately be written as:

$$V \simeq \frac{I\rho L \cos \theta}{2\pi r^2}$$
(2.17)

If r is greater than $3L$, the error of neglecting the higher-order terms is less than 3%. Thus, the potential is equal to that of a dipole of moment $I\rho L/2\pi$. Hence, the electric field can be written as:

$$E_r = -\frac{\partial V}{\partial r} = \frac{I\rho L \cos \theta}{\pi r^3} \qquad \text{(radial)}$$

$$E_\theta = -\frac{1}{r}\frac{\partial V}{\partial \theta} = \frac{I\rho L \sin \theta}{2\pi r^3} \qquad \text{(azimuthal)}$$

$$E_x = -\frac{\partial V}{\partial x} = \frac{I\rho L}{2\pi}\frac{3 \cos^2 \theta - 1}{r^3} \qquad \text{(parallel)}$$

$$E_y = -\frac{\partial V}{\partial y} = \frac{3}{2}\frac{I\rho L}{\pi}\frac{\sin \theta \cos \theta}{r^3} \qquad \text{(perpendicular)}$$
(2.18)

The electric field can be measured by means of two electrodes, M and N, as shown in Fig.4 for different orientations. If the distance l is small, then we can write: $E \simeq \Delta V/l$. Thus, from the relations (2.18), the resistivity of the ground can be determined.

When $\theta = 90°$, we get the electric field for the "equatorial arrangement", given by:

$$E_{\text{eq}} = \frac{I\rho L}{2\pi r^3}$$
(2.19)

and when $\theta = 0°$, we get the electric field for the "axial arrangement", given by:

$$E_{\text{ax}} = \frac{I\rho L}{\pi r^3}$$
(2.20)

Of the various dipole arrangements, the last two, i.e., the equatorial and the axial arrangements, are commonly used for dipole sounding.

Dipole sounding was suggested by Al'pin as early as 1940, although the usefulness of this method was not established until about 1956. The dipole method is now used extensively in the U.S.S.R. for deep electrical soundings (i.e., for depths more than 1 km).

Apparent resistivity

Using the formulas given so far, we can find out the resistivity of a semi-infinite homogeneous earth by means of any of the electrode arrangements discussed earlier. For an inhomogeneous medium we define a quantity $\bar{\rho}$, known as the *apparent resistivity*. The apparent resistivity of a geologic formation is equal to the true resistivity of a fictitious homogeneous and isotropic medium in which, for a given electrode arrangement and current strength I, the measured potential difference V is equal to that for the given inhomogeneous medium. The apparent resistivity depends upon the geometry and resistivities of the elements constituting the given geologic medium. Thus: $\bar{\rho} = K(\Delta V/I)$ where K is the geometrical coefficient having the dimension of length (m). For the different arrangements discussed in the section on current flow in a homogeneous earth, the values of K will be as given below:

(*1*) Symmetrical:

$$K_{\mathrm{w}} = 6.28a \qquad \text{(Wenner)}$$

$$K_{\mathrm{S}} = 0.785 \frac{(L + l)(L - l)}{l} \quad \text{(Schlumberger)}$$

(*2*) Dipole:

Radial:

$$K_r = \frac{\pi r^3}{Ll \cos \theta}$$

Azimuthal:

$$K_\theta = \frac{2\pi r^3}{Ll \sin \theta}$$

Parallel:

$$K_x = \frac{2\pi r^3}{Ll} \frac{1}{3 \cos^2 \theta - 1}$$

Perpendicular: $$K_y = \frac{2\pi r^3}{3Ll} \frac{1}{\sin\theta\cos\theta}$$

Equatorial: $$K_{eq} = \frac{2\pi r^3}{Ll}$$

Axial: $$K_{ax} = \frac{\pi r^3}{Ll}$$

CURRENT FLOW IN A HOMOGENEOUS ANISOTROPIC EARTH

It has been shown that in a homogeneous anisotropic medium the conductivity forms a symmetrical tensor characterised by six components. In such a case, it is always possible to orient the coordinate axes in such a way that $\sigma_{xy} = \sigma_{yz} = \sigma_{zx} = 0$. These axes are then called the "principal axes of anisotropy", and the principal values of J and E are then given by:

$$J_x = \frac{1}{\rho_x} E_x; \quad J_y = \frac{1}{\rho_y} E_y; \quad J_z = \frac{1}{\rho_z} E_z$$

where x, y, z are now the principal axes. Thus, the equation of continuity (2.2) may be written in terms of the principal axes as:

$$\frac{\partial}{\partial x}\left(\frac{E_x}{\rho_x}\right) + \frac{\partial}{\partial y}\left(\frac{E_y}{\rho_y}\right) + \frac{\partial}{\partial z}\left(\frac{E_z}{\rho_z}\right) = 0$$

For a homogeneous medium this reduces to:

$$\frac{1}{\rho_x} \frac{\partial^2 V}{\partial x^2} + \frac{1}{\rho_y} \frac{\partial^2 V}{\partial y^2} + \frac{1}{\rho_z} \frac{\partial^2 V}{\partial z^2} = 0 \qquad (2.21)$$

Choose a new system of coordinates, such that:

$$\xi = x\sqrt{\rho_x}; \quad \eta = y\sqrt{\rho_y}; \quad \zeta = z\sqrt{\rho_z}$$

then eq.(2.21) reduces to Laplace's equation:

$$\frac{\partial^2 V}{\partial\xi^2} + \frac{\partial^2 V}{\partial\eta^2} + \frac{\partial^2 V}{\partial\zeta^2} = 0$$

the solution of which is:

$$V = \frac{C}{(\xi^2 + \eta^2 + \zeta^2)^{\frac{1}{2}}}$$

where C is the constant of integration. Thus, the solution to eq.(2.21) is:

$$V = \frac{C}{(\rho_x x^2 + \rho_y y^2 + \rho_z z^2)^{\frac{1}{2}}} \qquad (2.22)$$

It is seen from eq.(2.22) that the equipotential surfaces given by:

$$\rho_x x^2 + \rho_y y^2 + \rho_z z^2 = K^2$$

are ellipsoids, the axes of which coincide with the principal axes of anisotropy. The current densities are given by:

$$\left. \begin{aligned}
J_x &= -\frac{1}{\rho_x}\frac{\partial V}{\partial x} = \frac{Cx}{(\rho_x x^2 + \rho_y y^2 + \rho_z z^2)^{\frac{3}{2}}} \\[2mm]
J_y &= -\frac{1}{\rho_y}\frac{\partial V}{\partial y} = \frac{Cy}{(\rho_x x^2 + \rho_y y^2 + \rho_z z^2)^{\frac{3}{2}}} \\[2mm]
J_z &= -\frac{1}{\rho_z}\frac{\partial V}{\partial z} = \frac{Cz}{(\rho_x x^2 + \rho_y y^2 + \rho_z z^2)^{\frac{3}{2}}}
\end{aligned} \right\} \qquad (2.23)$$

These equations satisfy the relation:

$$\frac{J_x}{x} = \frac{J_y}{y} = \frac{J_z}{z}$$

showing that the current lines are straight lines, spreading out radially from the source, as in the case of an isotropic medium.

The electric lines of force in an anisotropic medium form a family of curvilinear trajectories orthogonal to the equipotential surfaces. They do not coincide with the directions of the current lines except along the principal axes.

The anisotropy in a geological body may be due to several reasons. Thus, it is a well-known fact that in stratified rocks the strike offers a particularly favourable path for the flow of electric currents. The reason may be that a large number of mineral crystals possess a flat or elongated shape (mica, kaolin, etc.). At the time of their precipitation, they naturally take an orientation parallel to the sedimentation. The weathered surface soil, owing to vegetable matter, growth and decay of minerals in the soil, etc., also manifests an anisotropic character. In electrical exploration, the usual practice is to characterise the electrical property of a stratified rock by two parameters, namely, the longitudinal resistivity ρ_s (parallel to the plane of stratification) and the transverse resistivity ρ_t (normal to the plane of stratification). Thus any anisotropy in the plane of stratification is usually neglected, being very small in most practical cases.

If the plane of stratification is chosen as the xy plane, then eq.(2.21) reduces to:

$$\frac{1}{\rho_s}\left(\frac{\partial^2 V}{\partial x^2} + \frac{\partial^2 V}{\partial y^2}\right) + \frac{1}{\rho_t}\frac{\partial^2 V}{\partial z^2} = 0 \qquad (2.24)$$

The equipotential surfaces are then given by:

$$x^2 + y^2 + (\rho_t/\rho_s)z^2 = \text{constant}$$

i.e., they are ellipsoids of revolution around the z-axis.

We define two more parameters of an anisotropic medium:

$$\lambda = \sqrt{\rho_t/\rho_s} \text{ and } \rho_m = \sqrt{\rho_t\rho_s} \qquad (2.25)$$

where λ is called the "coefficient of anisotropy" and ρ_m the "root mean square resistivity", or simply the "mean resistivity" of the medium. It is obvious from eq.(2.25) that:

$$\rho_m = \lambda\rho_s = \frac{1}{\lambda}\rho_t \qquad (2.26)$$

The solution of eq.(2.24) may now be written as:

$$V = \frac{C}{\rho_s^{\frac{1}{2}}(x^2 + y^2 + \lambda^2 z^2)^{\frac{1}{2}}} \qquad (2.27)$$

and the current densities are:

$$J_x = \frac{Cx}{\rho_s^{\frac{3}{2}}(x^2 + y^2 + \lambda^2 z^2)^{\frac{3}{2}}}$$

$$J_y = \frac{Cy}{\rho_s^{\frac{2}{3}}(x^2 + y^2 + \lambda^2 z^2)^{\frac{3}{2}}}$$

$$J_z = \frac{Cz}{\rho_s^{\frac{2}{3}}(x^2 + y^2 + \lambda^2 z^2)^{\frac{3}{2}}}$$

such that:

$$J = (J_x^2 + J_y^2 + J_z^2)^{\frac{1}{2}} = \frac{C(x^2 + y^2 + z^2)^{\frac{1}{2}}}{\rho_s^{\frac{2}{3}}(x^2 + y^2 + \lambda^2 z^2)^{\frac{3}{2}}} \tag{2.28}$$

In order to find the constant of integration C, we construct around P a sphere of radius R and calculate the total current flowing out through this spherical surface.

This obviously is equal to the total current at the electrode P. Thus:

$$I = \int_s J \, ds = \int_0^{2\pi} \int_0^{\pi} J R^2 \sin \theta \, d\theta \, d\varphi \tag{2.29}$$

Now: $x^2 + y^2 = R^2 \sin^2 \theta$ and $z^2 = R^2 \cos^2 \theta$, then eq.(2.28) becomes:

$$J = \frac{C}{\rho_s^{\frac{2}{3}} R^2 (\sin^2 \theta + \lambda^2 \cos^2 \theta)^{\frac{3}{2}}} = \frac{C}{\rho_s^{\frac{2}{3}} R^2 \{1 + (\lambda^2 - 1) \cos^2 \theta\}^{\frac{3}{2}}}$$

and:

$$I = \frac{C}{\rho_s^{\frac{2}{3}}} \int_0^{2\pi} d\varphi \int_0^{\pi} \frac{\sin \theta \, d\theta}{\{1 + (\lambda^2 - 1) \cos^2 \theta\}^{\frac{3}{2}}}$$

$$= \frac{2\pi C}{\rho_s^{\frac{2}{3}}} \frac{2}{\lambda} = \frac{4\pi C}{\lambda \rho_s^{\frac{2}{3}}}$$

Therefore:

$$C = \frac{I}{4\pi} \lambda \rho_s^{\frac{2}{3}} \tag{2.30}$$

and, consequently, eq.(2.27) and (2.28) become:

$$V = \frac{I \lambda \rho_s}{4\pi (x^2 + y^2 + \lambda^2 z^2)^{\frac{1}{2}}} = \frac{I \rho_m}{4\pi R \{1 + (\lambda^2 - 1) \cos^2 \theta\}^{\frac{1}{2}}} \tag{2.31}$$

and:

$$J = \frac{I \lambda (x^2 + y^2 + z^2)^{\frac{1}{2}}}{4\pi (x^2 + y^2 + \lambda^2 z^2)^{\frac{3}{2}}} = \frac{I \lambda}{4\pi R^2 \{1 + (\lambda^2 - 1) \cos^2 \theta\}^{\frac{3}{2}}} \tag{2.32}$$

For an isotropic infinite homogeneous medium: $\lambda = 1$, $\rho_m = \rho$, and: $V = \rho I/4\pi R$ and $J = I/4\pi R^2$, as given in the section on a homogeneous earth.

Let us now put the point source of current I on the surface of the ground, which is assumed to be homogeneous but is anisotropic. Assuming that air has infinite resistivity, the current density in air is zero. The value of V and J are still given by eq.(2.27) and (2.28), but the value of C is now determined by finding the total current flow through a hemisphere of radius R, i.e., instead of eq.(2.29) we shall have:

$$I = \int_s J \, ds = \int_0^{2\pi} \int_0^{\pi/2} JR^2 \sin \theta \, d\theta \, d\varphi$$

giving:

$$C = \frac{I}{2\pi} \lambda \rho_s^{\frac{3}{2}}$$

Thus relations (2.31) and (2.32) are replaced by:

$$V = \frac{I}{2\pi R} \frac{\rho_m}{\{1 + (\lambda^2 - 1)\cos^2 \theta\}^{\frac{1}{2}}} = \frac{I\rho_m}{2\pi} \frac{1}{(x^2 + y^2 + \lambda^2 z^2)^{\frac{1}{2}}} \quad (2.33)$$

and:

$$J = \frac{I}{2\pi R^2} \frac{\lambda}{\{1 + (\lambda^2 - 1)\cos^2 \theta\}^{\frac{3}{2}}} = \frac{I\lambda}{2\pi} \frac{R}{(x^2 + y^2 + \lambda^2 z^2)^{\frac{3}{2}}} \quad (2.34)$$

As in case of an infinite medium, here, also, the equipotential surfaces are ellipsoids of revolution about the axis of z, i.e., perpendicular to the plane of stratification.

In eq.(2.33) and (2.34) we have assumed that the air-earth boundary is parallel to the plane of stratification. In order to generalize the formulas, we take two systems of coordinate, $x'y'z'$ and xyz (Fig.5), in which $x'y'$ represent the air–earth boundary and xy the plane of stratification, such that the strike of the bed x is taken as x' of the new system. Let the angle of dip be α.

Now:

$$x = x'$$
$$y = y' \cos \alpha + z' \sin \alpha$$
$$z = -y' \sin \alpha + z' \cos \alpha$$

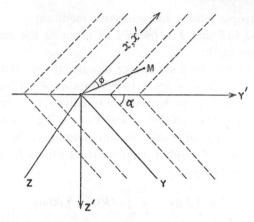

Fig.5. Anisotropic half-space. xy = plane of stratification; $x'y'$ = air–earth boundary surface; α = dip of the bed; φ = angle made by the point of observation with the strike direction.

Introducing the new coordinate system, and putting $z' = 0$, we get from eq.(2.33):

$$V = \frac{I\rho_m}{2\pi} \frac{1}{(x'^2 + y'^2 \cos^2 \alpha + \lambda^2 y'^2 \sin^2 \alpha)^{\frac{1}{2}}}$$

$$= \frac{I\rho_m}{2\pi} \frac{1}{[x'^2 + \{1 + (\lambda^2 - 1)\sin^2 \alpha\}y'^2]^{\frac{1}{2}}}$$

Writing $r^2 = x'^2 + y'^2$ and $\tan \varphi = y'/x'$, we get:

$$V = \frac{I\rho_m}{2\pi r} \frac{1}{\{1 + (\lambda^2 - 1)\sin^2 \varphi \sin^2 \alpha\}^{\frac{1}{2}}} \qquad (2.35)$$

Eq.(2.35) gives the potential at any point (M) on the surface, at a distance r from the source, and in the direction which makes an angle φ with the strike direction.

It is seen from eq.(2.35) that the equipotential lines on the surface are ellipses, with major axes oriented along the strike direction. The ratio of the semi-major to semi-minor axes are given by:

$$a/b = \{1 + (\lambda^2 - 1)\sin^2 \alpha\}^{\frac{1}{2}} \qquad (2.36)$$

which depends on the coefficient of anisotropy and the angle of dip. In the case of an isotropic medium (i.e., $\lambda = 1$), as also for horizontal beds (i.e., $\alpha = 0$), $a/b = 1$. Thus, in these cases the equipotential lines are circles about the source. For $\alpha = \pi/2$, $a = b\lambda$.

The formula (2.36) can be used to determine the coefficient of anisotropy (λ), when the dip of the beds is known, or conversely to determine the dip angle α when the anisotropy is known. The experimental procedure would be to draw the equipotential line and then determine the ratio of the axes a/b.

Differentiating eq.(2.35) with respect to r, we get the radial component of the electric field:

$$E = -\frac{\partial V}{\partial r} = \frac{I\rho_m}{2\pi r^2} \frac{1}{\{1 + (\lambda^2 - 1)\sin^2\varphi\sin^2\alpha\}^{\frac{1}{2}}} \qquad (2.37)$$

Defining apparent resistivity ($\bar\rho$), as in the case of an isotropic medium for a symmetrical Schlumberger spread, i.e., $\bar\rho = (E/I)2\pi r^2$, we get:

$$\bar\rho = \frac{\rho_m}{\{1 + (\lambda^2 - 1)\sin^2\varphi\sin^2\alpha\}^{\frac{1}{2}}} \qquad (2.38)$$

It follows that, along the strike direction:

$$\varphi = 0; \quad \bar\rho_s = \rho_m \qquad (2.39)$$

and normal to the strike direction, $\varphi = \pi/2$:

$$\bar\rho_t = \frac{\rho_m}{\{1 + (\lambda^2 - 1)\sin^2\alpha\}^{\frac{1}{2}}} \qquad (2.40)$$

Thus, the apparent resistivity, measured on the surface of a homogeneous anisotropic formation along the strike direction, is independent of the dip —eq.(2.39)— and is numerically equal to the mean resistivity of the formation. However, the apparent resistivity normal to the strike direction —eq.(2.40)— is dependent on the dip. Also, since the denominator of eq.(2.40) is greater than unity (except when $\alpha = 0$), it follows that except for $\alpha = 0$:

$$\bar\rho_t < \bar\rho_s \qquad (2.41)$$

For the special case $\alpha = \pi/2$:

$$\bar{\rho}_t = \rho_m/\lambda = \bar{\rho}_s \qquad (2.42)$$

From relation (2.41) it follows that the apparent resistivity $\bar{\rho}_t$, measured normal to the strike direction, is less than $\bar{\rho}_s$, measured along the strike direction—although it is known that the true resistivity of an anisotropic formation, normal to its stratification, is greater than that parallel to the plane of stratification. This phenomenon is called the "paradox of anisotropy".

The paradox is explained by the fact that since $\rho_s < \rho_t$, the current density along the plane of stratification is greater than that along the normal to this plane.

The anisotropy studied so far in this section characterizes finely stratified rocks which appear homogeneous to the eye and, in fact, in numerous cases this corresponds to a real homogeneity in composition. This type of anisotropy is microscopic and may be called "micro-anisotropy". In electrical prospecting it is necessary to consider a second kind of anisotropy, which may be called "macro-anisotropy". In practice it is sometimes difficult to draw the boundary between the micro- and the macro-anisotropy.

We may call a medium macro-anisotropic so long as the layers can be distinguished—for example, by electrical logging in a borehole. The concept of macro-anisotropy will be explained in brief in the next few paragraphs.

Macro-anisotropy results from the repetitive alternation of two different isotropic lithologic facies. When the individual layers become infinitely thin and infinitely repetitive, we obviously reach the domain of micro-anisotropy. The study of this parameter is of primary importance to the geophysicist, because the distribution of the electric field, due to two current electrodes at the surface of the ground, will be governed by the resistivity and thickness of the underlying layers in addition to the distance between the current electrodes. This effective resistivity and effective thickness are controlled by anisotropy.

In electrical prospecting, the two parameters of importance are: resistivity parallel to stratification (ρ_s), and resistivity normal to stratification (ρ_t); the physical significance of these has already been explained. Consequently, it is found that by adopting the concept of ρ_s and ρ_t for a group of layers, we are concerned with an anisotropy phenomenon; and the layers may be considered to behave as a single anisotropic layer of pseudo- or equivalent anisotropy λ. This anisotropic fictitious layer may be taken to be equivalent to another, single isotropic layer, of pseudo-resistivity ρ_e and pseudo-thickness h_e. This forms the basis of the analytic-graphical auxiliary-point method of interpretation, which will be dealt with in detail in Chapter 3.

CURRENT FLOW IN A HORIZONTALLY STRATIFIED EARTH

In electrical prospecting it is often necessary to determine the depth and the electrical resistivity of horizontal or nearly horizontal layers. In order to solve this problem, we should calculate the potential and the electric field, due to a point source of current, at any point on the surface of a stratified earth.

Let us choose a cylindrical system of coordinates, with the origin at the point source A, and the z-axis vertically downward normal

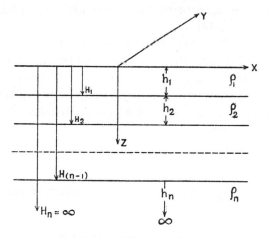

Fig.6. A multi-layer earth.

to the surface (Fig.6). Let $\rho_1, \rho_2 \ldots \rho_n$ be the resistivities, and $h_1, h_2 \ldots h_n$ be the thicknesses of the n layers from the top. Also, let $H_1, H_2 \ldots H_n$ denote the depths of the bottoms of each layer. We shall assume that the lowermost layer extends to infinity, i.e., $h_n = \infty$, $H_n = \infty$.

The Laplace equation to be satisfied at any point is:

$$\frac{\partial^2 V}{\partial r^2} + \frac{1}{r}\frac{\partial V}{\partial r} + \frac{\partial^2 V}{\partial z^2} = 0 \qquad (2.43)$$

the general solution of which may be written as:

$$V = \int_0^\infty \{A(m)e^{-mz} + B(m)e^{mz}\}J_0(mr)\,dm \qquad (2.44)$$

We know that the potential due to a point source of current placed on the surface of a homogeneous earth is:

$$V_0 = \frac{I\rho}{2\pi}\frac{1}{R} = \frac{I\rho}{2\pi}\frac{1}{(r^2 + z^2)^{\frac{1}{2}}}$$

The potential due to the point source at any point in the layered earth may be thought of as the sum of the potentials in a homogeneous medium and a perturbation potential, due to the boundaries, given by eq.(2.44).

Then: $V_1 = V_0 + V_1'$; $V_2 = V_0 + V_2'$; $V_i = V_0 + V_i'$; and $V_n = V_0 + V_n'$ where $V_1, V_2 \ldots V_n$ are the total potentials in the different strata, and $V_1', V_2' \ldots V_n'$ are the perturbation potentials. Perturbation potential may be physically explained as the contribution due to two series of an infinite number of images on both sides of the boundaries.

Thus, in general:

$$V_i = \frac{I\rho_1}{2\pi}\frac{1}{(r^2 + z^2)^{\frac{1}{2}}} + \int_0^\infty \{A_i(m)e^{-mz} + B_i(m)e^{mz}\}J_0(mr)\,dm \quad (2.45)$$

The constants A_i, B_i may be determined from the respective boundary conditions. At the air–earth boundary, we must have:

$$\frac{1}{\rho_1} \frac{\partial V_1}{\partial z} = 0 \text{ at } z = 0.$$

Now:

$$V_1 = \frac{I\rho_1}{2\pi} \frac{1}{(r^2 + z^2)^{\frac{1}{2}}} + \int_0^\infty (A_1 e^{-mz} + B_1 e^{mz}) J_0(mr) \, dm$$

Therefore:

$$\left(\frac{\partial V_1}{\partial z}\right)_{z=0} = \left\{ \frac{I\rho_1 z}{2\pi(r^2 + z^2)^{\frac{3}{2}}} + \int_0^\infty (-A_1 e^{-mz} + B_1 e^{mz}) J_0(mr) m \, dm \right\}_{z=0}$$

$$= \int_0^\infty (B_1 - A_1) J_0(mr) m \, dm = 0$$

Since the relation must be true for any value of r, $B_1 - A_1 = 0$, i.e., $B_1 = A_1$, then:

$$V_1 = \frac{I\rho_1}{2\pi} \frac{1}{(r^2 + z^2)^{\frac{1}{2}}} + \int_0^\infty A_1(m)(e^{mz} + e^{-mz}) J_0(mr) \, dm$$

Again, in the last layer, the potential must reduce to zero at $z = \infty$; i.e., $B_n = 0$, and:

$$V_n = \frac{I\rho_1}{2\pi} \frac{1}{(r^2 + z^2)^{\frac{1}{2}}} + \int_0^\infty A_n(m) e^{-mz} J_0(mr) \, dm$$

The boundary conditions to be satisfied at any boundary are:

$$V_i = V_{i+1}$$

$$\frac{1}{\rho_i} \frac{\partial V_i}{\partial z} = \frac{1}{\rho_{i+1}} \frac{\partial V_{i+1}}{\partial z} \text{ at } z = H_i \qquad (2.46)$$

We have $2n$ equations, and we have to determine $2n$ unknowns. Thus the problem can be solved uniquely.

Now:

$$\frac{1}{R} = \frac{1}{(r^2 + z^2)^{\frac{1}{2}}}$$

may be expressed in terms of the well-known Weber's integral formula:

$$\frac{1}{(r^2 + z^2)^{\frac{1}{2}}} = \int_0^\infty e^{-m|z|} J_0(mr)\,dm \tag{2.47}$$

and putting $I\rho_1/2\pi = q$, we get:

$$
\left.
\begin{aligned}
V_1 &= q \int_0^\infty e^{-m|z|} J_0(mr)\,dm \\
&\quad + \int_0^\infty A_1(m)(e^{mz} + e^{-mz})J_0(mr)\,dm \\
V_i &= q \int_0^\infty e^{-m|z|} J_0(mr)\,dm \\
&\quad + \int_0^\infty (A_i(m)e^{-mz} + B_i(m)e^{mz})J_0(mr)\,dm \\
V_n &= q \int_0^\infty e^{-m|z|} J_0(mr)\,dm \\
&\quad + \int_0^\infty A_n(m)e^{-mz} J_0(mr)\,dm
\end{aligned}
\right\} \tag{2.48}
$$

From relations (2.46) and (2.48) we get the following systems of equations:

$$
\left.
\begin{aligned}
&\int_0^\infty A_1 (e^{mH_1} + e^{-mH_1})J_0(mr)\,dm \\
&\qquad = \int_0^\infty (A_2 e^{-mH_1} + B_2 e^{mH_1})J_0(mr)\,dm \\
&-\frac{q}{\rho_1}\int_0^\infty e^{-mH_1}J_0(mr)\,dm + \frac{1}{\rho_1}\int_0^\infty A_1(e^{mH_1} - e^{-mH_1})J_0(mr)\,dm \\
&\qquad = -\frac{q}{\rho_2}\int_0^\infty e^{-mH_1} J_0(mr)\,dm \\
&\qquad\quad + \frac{1}{\rho_2}\int_0^\infty (-A_2 e^{-mH_1} + B_2 e^{mH_1})J_0(mr)\,dm
\end{aligned}
\right\} \tag{2.49a}
$$

$$\int_0^\infty (A_i e^{-mH_i} + B_i e^{mH_i}) J_0(mr) dm$$

$$= \int_0^\infty (A_{i+1} e^{-mH_i} + B_{i+1} e^{mH_i}) J_0(mr) dm$$

$$- \frac{q}{\rho_i} \int_0^\infty e^{-mH_i} J_0(mr) dm$$

$$+ \frac{1}{\rho_i} \int_0^\infty (-A_i e^{-mH_i} + B_i e^{mH_i}) J_0(mr) dm \qquad (2.49b)$$

$$= - \frac{q}{\rho_{i+1}} \int_0^\infty e^{-mH_i} J_0(mr) dm$$

$$+ \frac{1}{\rho_{i+1}} \int_0^\infty (-A_{i+1} e^{-mH_i} + B_{i+1} e^{mH_i}) J_0(mr) dm$$

$$\int_0^\infty (A_{n-1} e^{-mH_{n-1}} + B_{n-1} e^{mH_{n-1}}) J_0(mr) dm$$

$$= \int_0^\infty A_n e^{-mH_{n-1}} J_0(mr) dm$$

$$\frac{1}{\rho_{n-1}} \int_0^\infty (-A_{n-1} e^{-mH_{n-1}} + B_{n-1} e^{mH_{n-1}}) J_0(mr) dm$$

$$- \frac{q}{\rho_{n-1}} \int_0^\infty e^{-mH_{n-1}} J_0(mr) dm \qquad (2.49c)$$

$$= - \frac{q}{\rho_n} \int_0^\infty e^{-mH_{n-1}} J_0(mr) dm$$

$$- \frac{1}{\rho_n} \int_0^\infty A_n e^{-mH_{n-1}} J_0(mr) dm$$

As the relations (2.49a, b, c) should be valid for all values of r:

$$A_1(e^{-mH_1} + e^{mH_1}) - A_2\,e^{-mH_1} - B_2\,e^{mH_1} = 0$$

$$A_1\rho_2(e^{mH_1} - e^{-mH_1}) + A_2\rho_1\,e^{-mH_1}$$
$$- B_2\rho_1\,e^{mH_1} - q(\rho_2 - \rho_1)e^{-mH_1} = 0 \tag{2.50a}$$

$$A_i\,e^{-mH_i} + B_i\,e^{mH_i} - A_{i+1}\,e^{-mH_i} - B_{i+1}\,e^{mH_i} = 0$$

$$\rho_{i+1}(-A_i\,e^{-mH_i} + B_i\,e^{mH_i}) + \rho_i A_{i+1}\,e^{-mH_i}$$
$$- \rho_i B_{i+1}\,e^{mH_i} - q(\rho_{i+1} - \rho_i)e^{-mH_i} = 0 \tag{2.50b}$$

$$A_{n-1}\,e^{-mH_{n-1}} + B_{n-1}\,e^{mH_{n-1}} - A_n\,e^{-mH_{n-1}} = 0$$

$$-A_{n-1}\rho_n\,e^{-mH_{n-1}} + B_{n-1}\rho_n\,e^{mH_{n-1}}$$
$$+ A_n\rho_{n-1}\,e^{-mH_{n-1}} - q(\rho_n - \rho_{n-1})e^{-mH_{n-1}} = 0 \tag{2.50c}$$

Thus, from the system of eq.(2.50a, b, c), it is theoretically possible to find the potential, and hence the field, in any medium. In geo-electric sounding we are interested in finding only the potential on the surface, and it is sufficient to find out only the coefficient A_1 for some special cases of practical interest.

Homogeneous earth

$$A_1 = 0$$

and:

$$V = V_0 = \frac{I\rho}{2\pi}\,\frac{1}{(r^2 + z^2)^{\frac{1}{2}}} = \frac{I\rho}{2\pi}\,\frac{1}{R}$$

Two-layer earth

Put $h_2 = \infty$ in Fig.6, then the system of eq.(2.50a, b, c) reduce to:

$$A_1(e^{-mh_1} + e^{mh_1}) - A_2\,e^{-mh_1} = 0$$

$$A_1\rho_2(-e^{-mh_1} + e^{mh_1}) + A_2\rho_1\,e^{-mh_1} - q(\rho_2 - \rho_1)e^{-mh_1} = 0$$

Solving the equations and putting $(\rho_2 - \rho_1)/(\rho_2 + \rho_1) = K_{12}$, the reflection coefficient of the boundary, we get:

$$A_1(m) = q\,\frac{K_{12}\,e^{-2mh_1}}{1 - K_{12}\,e^{-2mh_1}}$$

$$= q(K_{12}\,e^{-2mh_1} + K_{12}^2\,e^{-4mh_1} + \cdots + K_{12}^n\,e^{-2mnh_1} + \cdots)$$

$$= q\sum_{n=1}^{\infty} K_{12}^n\,e^{-2mnh_1}$$

Hence:

$$V_1 = q \int_0^\infty e^{-mz} J_0(mr) dm$$

$$+ q \sum_{n=1}^\infty K_{12}^n \int_0^\infty e^{-2mnh_1}(e^{mz} + e^{-mz})J_0(mr)dm$$

Again using Weber's formula (2.47):

$$V_1 = \frac{q}{(r^2 + z^2)^{\frac{1}{2}}} + q \sum_{n=1}^\infty K_{12}^n \frac{1}{\{r^2 + (2nh_1 - z)^2\}^{\frac{1}{2}}}$$

$$+ q \sum_{n=1}^\infty K_{12}^n \frac{1}{\{r^2 + (2nh_1 + z)^2\}^{\frac{1}{2}}} \tag{2.51}$$

Eq.(2.51) gives the potential at any point (r, z) in the first medium. To find the potential on the surface, we put $z = 0$, then:

$$V = \frac{I\rho_1}{2\pi} \left[\frac{1}{r} + 2 \sum_{n=1}^\infty \frac{K_{12}^n}{\{r^2 + (2nh_1)^2\}^{\frac{1}{2}}} \right] \tag{2.52}$$

and the intensity on the surface, $E = -(\partial V/\partial r)$, is:

$$E = \frac{I\rho_1}{2\pi} \left[\frac{1}{r^2} + 2 \sum_{n=1}^\infty \frac{rK_{12}^n}{\{r^2 + (2nh_1)^2\}^{\frac{3}{2}}} \right] \tag{2.53}$$

The formulas (2.52) and (2.53) can be used to determine the apparent resistivity for any of the electrode arrangements given in the section on resistivity measurements.

Thus, for example, for the Wenner arrangement:

$$\Delta V = \frac{I\rho_1}{2\pi} \left[\frac{1}{a} + 4 \sum_{n=1}^\infty \frac{K_{12}^n}{\{a^2 + (2nh_1)^2\}^{\frac{1}{2}}} \right.$$

$$\left. - 4 \sum_{n=1}^\infty \frac{K_{12}^n}{\{(2a)^2 + (2nh_1)^2\}^{\frac{1}{2}}} \right]$$

$$= \frac{I\rho_1}{2\pi a} \left[1 + 4 \sum_{n=1}^\infty \frac{\delta K_{12}^n}{(\delta^2 + 4n^2)^{\frac{1}{2}}} - 4 \sum_{n=1}^\infty \frac{\delta K_{12}^n}{(4\delta^2 + 4n^2)^{\frac{1}{2}}} \right]$$

where: $\delta = a/h_1$. Therefore:

$$\bar{\rho} = 2\pi a \frac{\Delta V}{I} = \rho_1 \left[1 + 4 \sum_{n=1}^\infty \frac{\delta K_{12}^n}{(\delta^2 + 4n^2)^{\frac{1}{2}}} - 4 \sum_{n=1}^\infty \frac{\delta K_{12}^n}{(4\delta^2 + 4n^2)^{\frac{1}{2}}} \right]$$

$$\tag{2.54}$$

For the Schlumberger arrangement (for very small MN, i.e., $MN \to 0$):

$$\bar{\rho} = 2\pi r^2 \frac{E}{I} = \rho_1 \left[1 + 2 \sum_{n=1}^{\infty} \frac{\delta^3 K_{12}^n}{(\delta^2 + 4n^2)^{\frac{3}{2}}} \right] \qquad (2.55)$$

where: $\delta = r/h_1 = AB/2h_1$.

Three-layer earth

Put $h_3 = \infty$ in Fig.6, then the set of equations (2.50a, b, c) reduce to:

$$A_1(e^{-mH_1} + e^{mH_1}) - A_2 e^{-mH_1} - B_2 e^{mH_1} = 0$$

$$A_1\rho_2(-e^{-mH_1} + e^{mH_1}) + A_2\rho_1 e^{-mH_1}$$
$$- q(\rho_2 - \rho_1)e^{-mH_1} = 0$$

$$A_2 e^{-mH_2} + B_2 e^{mH_2} - A_3 e^{-mH_2} = 0 \qquad (2.56)$$

$$-A_2\rho_3 e^{-mH_2} + B_2\rho_3 e^{mH_2}$$
$$+ A_3\rho_2 e^{-mH_2} - q(\rho_3 - \rho_2)e^{-mH_2} = 0$$

Solving these equations we get:

$$A_1(m) = q \frac{K_{12}e^{-2mH_1} + K_{23}e^{-2mH_2}}{1 - K_{12}e^{-2mH_1} - K_{23}e^{-2mH_2} + K_{12}K_{23}e^{-2m(H_2-H_1)}}$$
$$(2.57)$$

where $K_{23} = (\rho_3 - \rho_2)/(\rho_3 + \rho_2)$.

Therefore:

$$V_1 = \frac{I\rho_1}{2\pi} \left[\frac{1}{(r^2 + z^2)^{\frac{1}{2}}} \right.$$

$$\left. + \int_0^{\infty} \frac{(K_{12}e^{-2mH_1} + K_{23}e^{-2mH_2})(e^{-mz} + e^{mz})J_0(mr)\,dm}{1 - K_{12}e^{-2mH_1} - K_{23}e^{-2mH_2} + K_{12}K_{23}e^{-2m(H_2-H_1)}} \right]$$
$$(2.58)$$

To express the potential in a convenient form for computation, we proceed in the following way:

Put, $H_1 = p_1H_0$ and $H_2 = p_2H_0$ where p_1 and p_2 are whole numbers, and H_0 has some fixed value.

Then, writing $e^{-2mH_0} = g$, eq.(2.57) may be written as:

$$A_1(m) = q \; \frac{K_{12}g^{p_1} + K_{23}g^{p_2}}{1 - K_{12}g^{p_1} - K_{23}g^{p_2} + K_{12}K_{23}g^{(p_2-p_1)}} \quad (2.59)$$

As p_1 and p_2 are whole numbers, $A_1(m)$ is a rational function of g, that is:

$$A_1(m) = q(b_1g + b_2g^2 + b_3g^3 + \ldots)$$

$$= q \sum_{n=1}^{\infty} b_n g^n = q \sum_{n-1}^{\infty} b_n e^{-2mnH_0} \quad (2.60)$$

Comparing eq.(2.59) and (2.60):

$$K_{12}g^{p_1} + K_{23}g^{p_2} = [1 - K_{12}g^{p_1} - K_{23}g^{p_2} + K_{12}K_{23}g^{(p_2-p_1)}] \sum_{n=1}^{\infty} b_n g^n$$

$$(2.61)$$

This identity requires that the coefficients of any order of g must be identically equal on both sides. As the highest order on the left-hand side is g^{p_2}, the coefficient of g of an order greater than p_2 on the right-hand side must be zero. Let us write down the coefficients of g^{p_2+m}, where m is a positive number, then:

$$b_{p_2+m} - K_{12}b_{p_2-p_1+m} - K_{23}b_m + K_{12}K_{23}b_{p_1+m} = 0$$

gives the recurrence formula:

$$b_{p_2+m} = K_{12}b_{p_2-p_1+m} + K_{23}b_m - K_{12}K_{23}b_{p_1+m} \quad (2.62)$$

Thus, b_{p_2+m} may be calculated, knowing the values of $b_{p_2-p_1+m}$, b_m and b_{p_1+m}. The coefficients up to the maximum value b_{p_2} may be determined from eq.(2.61). The rest of the coefficients can be determined through the use of the recurrence formula (2.62).

Thus the potential at any point in the first layer can be written as:

$$V_1 = \frac{I\rho_1}{2\pi} \left[\frac{1}{(r^2 + z^2)^{\frac{1}{2}}} + \sum_{n=1}^{\infty} \frac{b_n}{\{r^2 + (2nH_0 + z)^2\}^{\frac{1}{2}}} \right.$$

$$\left. + \sum_{n=1}^{\infty} \frac{b_n}{\{r^2 + (2nH_0 - z)^2\}^{\frac{1}{2}}} \right]$$

At the surface $z = 0$:

$$V = \frac{I\rho_1}{2\pi}\left[\frac{1}{r} + 2\sum_{n=1}^{\infty}\frac{b_n}{\{r^2 + (2nH_0)^2\}^{\frac{1}{2}}}\right] \tag{2.63}$$

and:

$$E = \frac{I\rho_1}{2\pi}\left[\frac{1}{r^2} + 2\sum_{n=1}^{\infty}\frac{b_n r}{\{r^2 + (2nH_0)^2\}^{\frac{3}{2}}}\right] \tag{2.64}$$

Thus, for the Schlumberger symmetrical arrangement:

$$\bar{\rho} = \rho_1\left[1 + 2\sum_{n=1}^{\infty}\frac{b_n r^3}{\{r^2 + (2nH_0)^2\}^{\frac{3}{2}}}\right]$$

In practice, the thickness of the second layer is usually expressed in terms of the thickness of the first layer, i.e., h_1. Then:

$$\bar{\rho} = \rho_1\left[1 + 2\sum_{n=1}^{\infty}\frac{b_n r^3}{\{r^2 + (2nH_1)^2\}^{\frac{3}{2}}}\right]$$

or if $r/h_1 = \delta$:

$$\bar{\rho} = \rho_1\left[1 + 2\sum_{n=1}^{\infty}\frac{b_n \delta^3}{(\delta^2 + 4n^2)^{\frac{3}{2}}}\right] \tag{2.65}$$

For the Wenner arrangement:

$$\bar{\rho} = \rho_1\left[1 + 4\sum_{n=1}^{\infty}\frac{b_n \delta}{(\delta^2 + 4n^2)^{\frac{1}{2}}} - 4\sum_{n=1}^{\infty}\frac{b_n \delta}{(4\delta^2 + 4n^2)^{\frac{1}{2}}}\right] \tag{2.66}$$

if $\delta = a/h_1$.

Four-layer earth

In the case of a four-layer earth, it can be shown that:

$$A_1(m) = \frac{q(K_{12}g^{p_1} + K_{23}g^{p_2} + K_{34}g^{p_3} + K_{12}K_{23}K_{34}g^{p_3-p_2-p_1})}{1 - K_{12}g^{p_1} - K_{23}g^{p_2} - K_{34}g^{p_3} + K_{12}K_{23}g^{p_2-p_1} +} \tag{2.67}$$
$$\overline{+ K_{23}K_{34}g^{p_3-p_2} + K_{12}K_{34}g^{p_3-p_1}}$$

Here, also, the potential can be expressed in the same form as eq.(2.63) and the apparent resistivity expressed in the form eq.(2.65). The complications in computation increase with the increase in the number of layers. With the use of computers it has been possible to plot sets of theoretical master curves to be used for interpretation. The method of computation of theoretical curves is beyond the scope of this book, as such sets of two-, three- and four-layer master curves are already available in published form (MOONEY and WETZEL, 1956; COMPAGNIE GÉNÉRALE DE GÉOPHYSIQUE, 1963; ANONYMOUS, 1963a, b, c; and ORELLANA and MOONEY, 1966).

The interested reader may refer to pp.9–12 of the COMPAGNIE GÉNÉRALE DE GÉOPHYSIQUE (1963) for a generalized approach to the computation of sets of three-layer master curves. However, the specific case of a simplified three-layer problem is added as an example at the end of this chapter.

It may be mentioned here that various simplified approaches to the computation of theoretical curves have been suggested from time to time. FLATHE (1955) introduced his method of calculating sounding curves with an ordinary desk calculator; but this is suitable only for cases approximated by a perfectly conducting and perfectly insulating substratum. VAN DAM (1965) has introduced a simple method for the calculation of sufficiently exact sounding curves with hand calculators.

A procedure to compute apparent resistivity curves for layered earth structure for the Schlumberger, Wenner and dipole configurations, has been given by MOONEY et al. (1966), where use is made of large digital computers. In this method, the formulation is relatively simple, and a single program can handle any number of layers; in addition, a single set of stored coefficients can be used repeatedly by different electrode spacing and for different electrode arrangements. The technique is claimed to be relatively simpler and more accurate compared to those described by the COMPAGNIE GÉNÉRALE DE GÉOPHYSIQUE (1955, 1963) and FLATHE (1955). However, the method suggested by VAN DAM (1967) is somewhat similar to the one described by MOONEY et al. (1966), and this method is meant for use with digital calculators.

PRINCIPLE OF EQUIVALENCE

In this section we shall give the theoretical basis of a result which, as we shall see later, serves a very important purpose in the interpretation of geoelectric sounding curves. This is known as the "principle of equivalence".

We know that the potential at the surface of a three-layer earth depends on the coefficient A_1 given by:

$$A_1(m) = q \frac{K_{12}\, e^{-2mh_1} + K_{23}\, e^{-2m(h_1+h_2)}}{1 - K_{12}\, e^{-2mh_1} - K_{23}\, e^{-2m(h_1+h_2)} + K_{12}K_{23}\, e^{-2mh_2}}$$

$$(2.68)$$

where $q = I\rho_1/2\pi$; K_{12} and K_{23} have usual meaning.

Case I

Let us suppose $h_2 \ll h_1$; $\rho_2 \ll \rho_1$ and $\rho_3 \gg \rho_2$, then:

$$e^{-2m(h_1+h_2)} = e^{-2mh_1}\, e^{-2mh_2} \simeq e^{-2mh_1}(1 - 2mh_2)$$

$$K_{12} = \frac{2\rho_2}{\rho_2 + \rho_1} - 1 \simeq \frac{2\rho_2}{\rho_1} - 1$$

$$K_{23} = 1 - \frac{2\rho_2}{\rho_3 + \rho_2} \simeq 1 - \frac{2\rho_2}{\rho_3}$$

Eq.(2.68) can be written as:

$$A_1(m) = q\, e^{-2mh_1}$$

$$\cdot \frac{\rho_3 - \rho_1 - m\rho_1\rho_3(h_2/\rho_2)}{-\left[\left(\dfrac{1}{\rho_1} - \dfrac{1}{\rho_3}\right) - m(h_2/\rho_2)\right]e^{-2mh_1} + \dfrac{1}{\rho_1} - \dfrac{1}{\rho_3} + m(h_2/\rho_2)}$$

$$= q\, e^{-2mh_1} \cdot \frac{\rho_3 - \rho_1 - m\rho_1\rho_3 S}{-(\rho_3 - \rho_1 - m\rho_1\rho_3 S)e^{-2mh_1} + \rho_3 - \rho_1 + m\rho_1\rho_3 S} \qquad (2.69)$$

It is seen from the relation (2.69) that $A_1(m)$ does not depend on the absolute values of ρ_2 and h_2, but only on the ratio $h_2/\rho_2 = S$.

Case II

Similarly, when $h_2 \ll h_1$; $\rho_2 \gg \rho_3$ and $\rho_2 \gg \rho_1$:

$$K_{12} = 1 - \frac{2\rho_1}{\rho_2 + \rho_1} \simeq 1 - \frac{2\rho_1}{\rho_2}$$

$$K_{23} = \frac{2\rho_3}{\rho_2 + \rho_3} - 1 \simeq \frac{2\rho_3}{\rho_2} - 1$$

and:

$$A_1(m) = q\,e^{-2mh_1} \cdot \frac{\rho_3 - \rho_1 + mT}{(\rho_1 - \rho_3 - mT)e^{-2mh_1} + \rho_1 + \rho_3 + mT} \qquad (2.70)$$

Here $A_1(m)$ depends only on $T = h_2\rho_2$ and not individually on ρ_2 and h_2.

Case I refers to an H-type section and case II refers to a K-type section, as will be explained in Chapter 3.

According to the above discussion, it can be said that H-type curves are "equivalent" with respect to S, provided the intermediate layer has a thickness and resistivity which is very small compared to those of the other two; and K-type curves are "equivalent" with respect to T if the thickness of the intermediate layer is small, but resistivity is large, compared to the other two layers.

The practical usefulness of the "principle of equivalence" in the interpretation of sounding data will be discussed in Chapter 3.

VERTICAL ELECTRICAL SOUNDING (V.E.S.)

We have seen that the apparent resistivity as measured on the surface of an inhomogeneous earth is given by:

$$\bar{\rho} = K\frac{\Delta V}{I}$$

where K, a geometrical factor, depends on the configuration of the current as well as measuring electrodes. Broadly speaking, we can distinguish two types of resistivity measurements. In the first, known as *geoelectric profiling* or mapping, the value of K remains constant for a particular set of readings, and measurements are done at various points on the surface. In this way, we get the surface variation of apparent resistivity values within a certain depth. In the second method, known as *geoelectric sounding*, for a particular set of readings the measurements are done at a specified point such that the value of K progressively changes. In this way, the apparent resistivity values at the surface reflect the vertical distribution of resistivity values in a geological section. This is why geoelectric sounding is sometimes known as "vertical electric drilling". The present book deals with the latter aspect of resistivity prospecting.

An arrangement of electrodes which is widely used is the symmetrical one, where current electrodes A, B are symmetrically placed with respect to the potential electrodes M, N (Fig.2), and where the centre of the spread, O, is the sounding point. In the Wenner method the sounding is done by progressively increasing the value of "a", the spread length, by moving all four electrodes outwards after each sounding. In the Schlumberger method the sounding may be done (theoretically speaking) by moving only the current electrodes, progressively increasing the distance AB. However when AB is very large compared to MN, the potential drop between M and N may be too small to be measured. Hence, in practice it is necessary also to increase the distance between M

TABLE I

A TYPICAL FIELD LAYOUT FOR SCHLUMBERGER ARRANGEMENT

Obser-vation number	$MN/2$ (m)	$AB/2$ (m)	Obser-vation number	$MN/2$ (m)	$AB/2$ (m)	obser-vation number	$MN/2$ (m)	$AB/2$ (m)
1	0.5	1.5	15	2	20	29	20	160
2	0.5	2	16	5	15	30	20	200
3	0.5	3	17	5	20	31	40	200
4	0.5	4	18	5	30	32	40	250
5	0.5	5	19	5	40	33	40	300
6	1	3	20	5	50	34	40	350
7	1	4	21	10	30	35	40	400
8	1	6	22	10	40	36	80	400
9	1	8	23	10	50	37	80	600
10	1	10	24	10	60	38	80	800
11	2	6	25	10	80	39	100	800
12	2	8	26	10	100	40	100	1000
13	2	10	27	20	100			
14	2	15	28	20	140			

and N, whenever required, depending on the sensitivity of the measuring instrument. The value of MN and the corresponding values of AB are chosen in order to get overlapping readings whenever a change-over of MN from one value to the other takes place. The usual distribution in the values of MN and AB for an average instrument sensitivity, and for a maximum spread $AB = 2,000$ m, is tabulated in Table I; this is subject to modification, depending on the field conditions, instrument sensitivity, and other practical difficulties. In the beginning, a few readings may be taken with the Wenner arrangement, so as to get the resistivity of the surface layers.

Sometimes, for shallow sounding, it is convenient to use the three-electrode system (AMN), where one of the current electrodes (B) is placed at infinity (AB at least ten times maximum AO), and the sounding is done by moving only the current electrode A. The theory of apparent resistivity for V.E.S. over a horizontally stratified earth, for Wenner as well as for Schlumberger arrangement, has already been dealt with.

DIPOLE ELECTRICAL SOUNDING (D.E.S.)

We have already discussed the various dipole arrangements for resistivity prospecting. We shall now derive expressions for the apparent resistivity in the case of a horizontally stratified earth for dipole electrical sounding (D.E.S.).

It has been shown that the potential V_0 on the surface of a horizontally stratified earth is given by —from eq.(2.63):

$$V_0 = \frac{I\rho_1}{2\pi} \left[\frac{1}{r} + 2 \sum_{n=1}^{\infty} \frac{b_n}{\{r^2 + (2nh_1)^2\}^{\frac{1}{2}}} \right] \quad (2.71)$$

For a dipole:

$$V_{\text{dipole}} = - \frac{\partial V_0}{\partial r} \frac{\partial r}{\partial L} L$$

$$= \frac{IL}{2\pi} \rho_1 \cos \theta \left[\frac{1}{r^2} + 2 \sum_{n=1}^{\infty} b_n \frac{r}{\{r^2 + (2nh_1)^2\}^{\frac{3}{2}}} \right] \quad (2.72)$$

and the field components are:

$$E_r = \frac{IL}{\pi} \rho_1 \cos\theta \left[\frac{1}{r^3} + \sum_{n=1}^{\infty} b_n \frac{2r^2 - (2nh_1)^2}{\{r^2 + (2nh_1)^2\}^{\frac{5}{2}}} \right] \qquad (2.73)$$

$$E_\theta = \frac{IL}{2\pi} \rho_1 \sin\theta \left[\frac{1}{r^3} + 2 \sum_{n=1}^{\infty} b_n \frac{1}{\{r^2 + (2nh_1)^2\}^{\frac{3}{2}}} \right] \qquad (2.74)$$

Comparing eq.(2.73) and (2.74) with eq.(2.18) we get the values of apparent resistivities, i.e., $\bar{\rho}_r$ and $\bar{\rho}_\theta$ given by:

$$\bar{\rho}_r = \rho_1 \left[1 + 2 \sum_{n=1}^{\infty} b_n \frac{r^3\{r^2 - 2(nh_1)^2\}}{\{r^2 + (2nh_1)^2\}^{\frac{5}{2}}} \right] \qquad (2.75)$$

$$\bar{\rho}_\theta = \rho_1 \left[1 + 2 \sum_{n=1}^{\infty} b_n \frac{r^3}{\{r^2 + (2nh_1)^2\}^{\frac{3}{2}}} \right] \qquad (2.76)$$

Writing $r/h_1 = \delta$:

$$\bar{\rho}_r/\rho_1 = 1 + 2 \sum_{n=1}^{\infty} b_n \frac{\delta^3(\delta^2 - 2n^2)}{(\delta^2 + 4n^2)^{\frac{5}{2}}} \qquad (2.77)$$

$$\bar{\rho}_\theta/\rho_1 = 1 + 2 \sum_{n=1}^{\infty} b_n \frac{\delta^3}{(\delta^2 + 4n^2)^{\frac{3}{2}}} \qquad (2.78)$$

In the case of conventional sounding by the symmetrical Schlumberger arrangement, we have—from eq.(2.65):

$$\bar{\rho}/\rho_1 = 1 + 2 \sum_{n=1}^{\infty} b_n \frac{\delta^3}{(\delta^2 + 4n^2)^{\frac{3}{2}}} \qquad (2.79)$$

A comparison of eq.(2.78) with (2.79) indicates that the expression for $\bar{\rho}_\theta/\rho_1$ for the dipole arrangement is the same as that for the symmetrical Schlumberger arrangement (for a horizontally stratified earth).

Thus, all the master curves available for conventional Schlumberger sounding may also be used for dipole azimuthal sounding, and the method of interpretation remains the same.

Now, differentiating eq.(2.79) with respect to δ, and multiplying by $\delta/2$, we get:

$$\frac{\delta}{2} \frac{\partial \bar{\rho}}{\partial \delta} = 2\rho_1 \sum_{n=1}^{\infty} b_n \frac{6n^2\delta^3}{(\delta^2 + 4n^2)^{\frac{5}{2}}}$$

Therefore:

$$\bar{\rho} - \frac{\delta}{2} \frac{\partial \bar{\rho}}{\partial \delta} = \rho_1 \left[1 + 2 \sum_{n=1}^{\infty} b_n \left\{ \frac{\delta^3}{(\delta^2 + 4n^2)^{\frac{3}{2}}} - \frac{6n^2\delta^3}{(\delta^2 + 4n^2)^{\frac{5}{2}}} \right\} \right]$$

$$= \rho_1 \left[1 + 2 \sum_{n=1}^{\infty} b_n \frac{\delta^3(\delta^2 - 2n^2)}{(\delta^2 + 4n^2)^{\frac{5}{2}}} \right] = \bar{\rho}_r \qquad (2.80)$$

Eq.(2.80) can be utilized graphically to construct the master curves for a radial dipole sounding arrangement from the curves available for the conventional symmetrical Schlumberger arrangement. Three-layer master curves for radial dipole arrangement are available in published form (ANONYMOUS, 1957).

Since both $\bar{\rho}_r$ and $\bar{\rho}_\theta$ are independent of angle θ for a horizontally stratified earth, it is obvious that formulas for $\bar{\rho}_r$ and $\bar{\rho}_\theta$ are valid for $\bar{\rho}_{ax}$ ($\bar{\rho}_r$, $\theta = 0$) and $\bar{\rho}_{eq}$ ($\bar{\rho}_\theta$, $\theta = 90°$), respectively.

Similarly, we can also find the apparent resistivity for the parallel and perpendicular arrangements of the dipole.

Hence, for a horizontally stratified earth, the apparent resistivity for any of the dipole arrangements may be obtained from the apparent resistivity of the conventional Schlumberger arrangement by means of the following formulas:

$$\bar{\rho}_r = \bar{\rho}_{ax} = \bar{\rho} - \frac{\delta}{2} \frac{\partial \bar{\rho}}{\partial \delta} \qquad (2.81)$$

$$\bar{\rho}_\theta = \bar{\rho}_{eq} = \bar{\rho} \qquad (2.82)$$

$$\bar{\rho}_x = \bar{\rho} - \frac{\delta \cos^2 \theta}{3 \cos^2 \theta - 1} \frac{\partial \bar{\rho}}{\partial \delta} \qquad (2.83)$$

$$\bar{\rho}_y = \bar{\rho} - \frac{\delta}{3} \frac{\partial \bar{\rho}}{\partial \delta} \qquad (2.84)$$

EXAMPLE (COMPUTATION PROCEDURE)

It has been shown in eq.(2.65) that for the Schlumberger arrangement:

$$\bar{\rho} = \rho_1 \left[1 + 2 \sum_{n=1}^{\infty} \frac{b_n \delta^3}{\{\delta^2 + (2n)^2\}^{\frac{3}{2}}} \right]$$

where the coefficient b_n is given by eq.(2.61); for $p_2 > p_1$ this is given by the recurrence formula represented by eq.(2.62). Once b_n is known, the value of $\bar{\rho}/\rho_1$ can easily be calculated for various values of δ (i.e., r/h_1) with the help of a computer, when expressed in the following way:

$$\bar{\rho}/\rho_1 = 1 + \frac{2b_1\delta^3}{(\delta^2 + 4)^{\frac{3}{2}}} + \frac{2b_2\delta^3}{(\delta^2 + 16)^{\frac{3}{2}}} + \ldots + \ldots$$

In the case of a three-layer problem, the computations are simplified when $\rho_3 = 0$ or ∞, because in that case the coefficient $A_1(m)$ given in eq.(2.59) is further simplified.

Let us consider a specific case with the following values:

$$\rho_1 = 100 \ \Omega m; \ \ \rho_2 = 5 \ \Omega m; \ \ \rho_3 = \infty;$$
$$h_1 = 10 \ m; \ \ h_2 = 10 \ m; \ \ h_3 = \infty.$$

Then $H_1 = h_1$ and $H_2 = 2h_1$, i.e., $p_1 = 1$; $p_2 = 2$.

From eq.(2.59), comparing with eq.(2.60), we can write the value of the coefficient $A_1(m)$ given by:

$$A_1 = \frac{K_{12}g + g^2}{1 - g^2} = \sum_{n=1}^{\infty} b_n g^n \qquad (2.85)$$

or:

$$A_1 = a \frac{g}{1 - g} + c \frac{-g}{1 + g}$$

such that: $(a - c) = K_{12}$; $(a + c) = 1$, or:

$$a = \frac{1 + K_{12}}{2}; \ \ c = \frac{1 - K_{12}}{2}$$

On expansion into a series:

$$A_1 = a(g + g^2 + g^3 + \ldots) + c(-g - g^2 - g^3 - \ldots) = \sum_{n=1}^{\infty} b_n g^n \qquad (2.86)$$

This gives $b_1 = b_2 = b_3 = 1$ for the first part, and $b_1 = b_2 = b_3 = (-1)$ for the second part, and the apparent resistivity $\bar{\rho}$ is given by:

$$\bar{\rho}/\rho_1 = 1 + \frac{1 + K_{12}}{2} \cdot 2 \sum_{n=1}^{\infty} \frac{\delta^3}{\{\delta^2 + (2n)^2\}^{\frac{3}{2}}}$$
$$+ \frac{1 - K_{12}}{2} \cdot 2 \sum_{n=1}^{\infty} \frac{\delta^3(-1)^n}{\{\delta^2 + (2n)^2\}^{\frac{3}{2}}} \tag{2.87}$$

The value of $\bar{\rho}/\rho_1$ can be computed from the above expression for a certain value of K_{12}, i.e., (ρ_2/ρ_1) for different values of $\delta = r/h_1 = = AB/2h_1$.

In the present case, $K_{12} = 0.905$, and the variables are δ and n. The value of n should be chosen properly, so as to increase the possibility of neglecting the effect of higher-order terms without appreciable error in the calculation. If the series is highly convergent, sufficient accuracy may be obtained within five to ten terms. However, for some unfavourable conditions it may be necessary to consider a much larger number of terms (50 or more).

The above relation (2.87), giving the value of $\bar{\rho}/\rho_1$, presents a very interesting point; and it can be still further simplified, giving rise to the possibility of using two-layer curves for plotting the three-layer curve.

In the case of two-layer earth, we know that for $\rho_2 = \infty$, the value of $\bar{\rho}$ is given by:

$$\bar{\rho}_\infty = \rho_1 \left[1 + 2 \sum_{n=1}^{\infty} \frac{\delta^3}{\{\delta^2 + (2n)^2\}^{\frac{3}{2}}} \right]$$

and, similarly, for $\rho_2 = 0$, we can write:

$$\bar{\rho}_0 = \rho_1 \left[1 + 2 \sum_{n=1}^{\infty} \frac{\delta^3(-1)^n}{\{\delta^2 + (2n)^2\}^{\frac{3}{2}}} \right]$$

Thus eq.(2.87) may be written as:

$$\bar{\rho} = \frac{1 - K_{12}}{2} \bar{\rho}_0 + \frac{1 + K_{12}}{2} \bar{\rho}_\infty \tag{2.88}$$

Therefore, eq.(2.88) indicates that we can plot the three-layer theoretical master curve for the given case with the help of the two-layer master curves available for $\rho_2 = 0$ and $\rho_2 = \infty$. The actual procedure for graphical construction of three- and four-layer curves is given in detail in Chapter 3. In practice, however, the formula (2.87) is directly used for programming and subsequent calculation by means of computers.

Schlumberger Sounding

The interpretation of geophysical field data requires a large number of theoretical master curves for different geological sections. The total number available for the purpose is, however, grossly inadequate. It is therefore necessary to find a rapid and reasonably accurate method of construction of suitable empirical master curves which may be used in cases where theoretical curves are not available.

This chapter first deals with the basic principles and procedures for the construction of such curves by the analytic-graphical method, which is found to be quite useful in practice. It then explains detailed techniques of interpretation, using the available theoretical master curves along with the "auxiliary point charts" and the "equivalent curves". The method of interpretation presented here deals only with the Schlumberger sounding. The interpretation of Wenner sounding curves will be explained in Chapter 4.

TYPE CURVES AND AVAILABLE THEORETICAL CURVES

Two-layer curves

Two sets of theoretical two-layer master curves are available for (ρ_2/ρ_1) greater than unity, i.e., ascending type (Set I) and for (ρ_2/ρ_1) less than unity, i.e., descending type (Set II). The values of ρ_2/ρ_1 for which curves have been plotted are:

Set I: $\rho_2/\rho_1 = 11/9, 3/2, 13/7, 2, 7/3, 3, 4, 5, 17/3, 7, 9, 19, 39, 99, \infty$.

Set II: ρ_2/ρ_1 = 9/11, 2/3, 7/13, 1/2, 3/7, 1/3, 1/4, 1/5, 3/17, 1/7, 1/9, 1/19, 1/39, 1/99, 0.

These sets of theoretical master curves have been reproduced in Plates I and II—plotted on a double-logarithm graph sheet with a modulus of 62.5 mm—and can be used for construction and interpretation of multi-layer curves. These sets are presented as master curves, chart 1s in the COMPAGNIE GÉNÉRALE DE GÉOPHYSI- QUE (1963) and as Paletka chart 1s in ANONYMOUS (1963a). ORELLANA and MOONEY (1966) have recently published a set of two-layer curves representing 25 such cases.

Three-layer curves

The whole set of three-layer sounding curves can be divided into four groups, depending on the relative values of ρ_1, ρ_2 and ρ_3:

(*1*) Minimum type: when $\rho_1 > \rho_2 < \rho_3$. This is also referred to as H-type (associated with the name of Hummel).

(*2*) Double ascending type: when $\rho_1 < \rho_2 < \rho_3$. This is also known as A-type (corresponding to the term anisotropy).

(*3*) Maximum type: when $\rho_1 < \rho_2 > \rho_3$. This is known as K-type or is sometimes referred to as DA-type (meaning displaced or modified anisotropy).

(*4*) Double descending type: when $\rho_1 > \rho_2 > \rho_3$. This is known as Q-type and is sometimes referred to as DH-type (meaning displaced Hummel or modified Hummel).

A diagrammatical representation of all these type curves is given in Fig.7 for the three-layer cases. The following theoretical three-layer master curves for Schlumberger configuration are available in published form: (*1*) The COMPAGNIE GÉNÉRALE DE GÉOPHYSIQUE (1955, 1963) contains 48 sets of curves, each set containing 10 curves, giving a total of 480 separate curves available for interpretation. (*2*) ANONYMOUS (1963a) contains 72 sets, each set containing 10 curves, making a total of 720 curves available for interpretation. (*3*) ORELLANA and MOONEY (1966) present master tables and curves representing 76 three-layer sets (25 each of H- and K-type and 13 each of Q- and A-type), with a total of 912

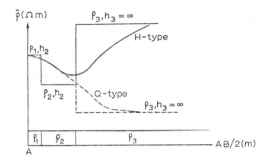

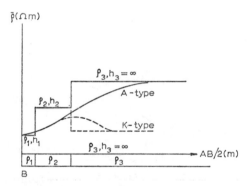

Fig.7. Three-layer type curves. A. H-type ($\rho_1 > \rho_2 < \rho_3$) and Q-type ($\rho_1 > > \rho_2 > \rho_3$). B. A-type ($\rho_1 < \rho_2 < \rho_3$) and K-type ($\rho_1 < \rho_2 > \rho_3$).

three-layer cases. The parameters of the curves in (1) and (2) are given below:

For H-type:

$$\rho_2/\rho_1 = 2/3, 3/7, 1/4, 1/9, 1/19 \text{ and } 1/39$$

and:

$$\rho_3/\rho_1 = \infty, 1 \text{ and } (\rho_2/\rho_1)^{\frac{1}{2}}$$

For A-type:

$$\rho_2/\rho_1 = 3/2, 7/3, 4, 9, 19 \text{ and } 39$$

and:

$$\rho_3/\rho_1 = \infty, (\rho_2/\rho_1)^2 \text{ and } (\rho_2/\rho_1)^{\frac{3}{2}}$$

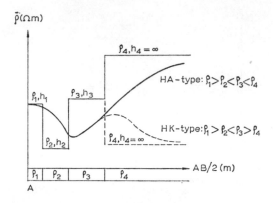

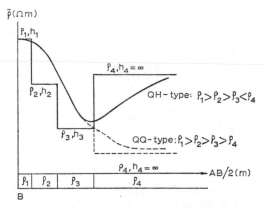

Fig.8. Nature of four-layer type curves. A. HA- and HK-type. B. QH- and QQ-type. C. KH- and KQ-type. D. AA- and AK-type.

For K-type:

$$\rho_2/\rho_1 = 3/2,\ 7/3,\ 4,\ 9,\ 19\ \text{and}\ 39$$

and:

$$\rho_3/\rho_1 = (\rho_2/\rho_1)^{\frac{1}{2}},\ 1\ \text{and}\ 0$$

For Q-type:

$$\rho_2/\rho_1 = 2/3,\ 3/7,\ 1/4,\ 1/9,\ 1/19\ \text{and}\ 1/39$$

and:

$$\rho_3/\rho_1 = (\rho_2/\rho_1)^{\frac{2}{3}},\ (\rho_2/\rho_1)\ \text{and}\ 0$$

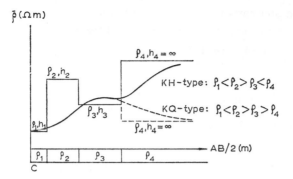

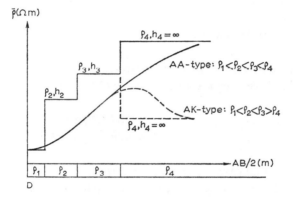

Fig.8 C, D (Legend see p.44).

Each set contains curves for ten different values of $h_2/h_1 = 1/9$, 1/5, 1/3, 1/2, 1, 2, 3, 5, 9, 24 and ∞. In the case of the curves by Orellana and Mooney, the model parameters are slightly different and are whole numbers or simple decimels.

Four-layer curves

From a combination of the curves of the types H, A, K and Q discussed above (Fig.7), it is easily seen that there can be only eight types of four-layer curves, shown in Fig.8. These may be designated as HA, HK; AA, AK; KH, KQ and QH, QQ. Theoretically plotted master curves for four-layer cases are available as "Paletka" in Anonymous (1963b). This album of four-layer theoretical master curves contains 122 sets, covering all the eight types. The values of the parameters are given below:

ρ_2/ρ_1 = 1/39, 1/19, 1/9, 3/17, 1/4, 3/7, 2/3, 3/2, 7/3, 17/3, 3, 4, 9 and 39

ρ_3/ρ_1 = 1/39, 1/19, 1/9, 3/17, 1/4, 3/7, 2/3, 3/2, 7/3, 17/3, 3, 4, 9 and 39

h_2/h_1 = 1/2, 1, 2, 3, 5, 24; h_3/h_1 = 1/2, 1, 2, 3, 10, 12 and 72

The four-layer curves published by ORELLANA and MOONEY (1966) consist of a total of 480 cases distributed in 30 sets.

ASYMPTOTIC VALUES OF SCHLUMBERGER CURVES

The apparent resistivity ($\bar{\rho}$) for a two-layer earth may be written, for Schlumberger arrangement—see eq.(2.55)—as:

$$\frac{\bar{\rho}}{\rho_1} = 1 + 2 \sum_{n=1}^{\infty} \frac{K_{12}^n (AB/2h_1)^3}{\{(AB/2h_1)^2 + (2n)^2\}^{\frac{3}{2}}} \tag{3.1}$$

Several limiting cases which can be derived from eq.(3.1) are:

(a) When $\rho_2 = \rho_1$, $\bar{\rho} = \rho_1$, i.e., the apparent resistivity is equal to the true resistivity of the semi-infinite medium .

(b) When $AB/2 \to 0$, $\bar{\rho} = \rho_1$, i.e., for a two-layer earth the apparent resistivity is equal to the true resistivity of the first layer for small values of electrode separation.

(c) When $AB/2 \to \infty$, $\bar{\rho} = \rho_2$, i.e., the apparent resistivity is equal to the true resistivity of the second layer for large values of electrode separation.

We can write eq.(3.1) in the form:

$$\bar{\rho} = \rho_1 f(AB/2h_1) \tag{3.2}$$

assuming that K_{12}, i.e., ρ_2/ρ_1 remains constant.

If we plot $\bar{\rho}$ against $AB/2h_1$ from eq.(3.2) on an arithmetic scale, we get different curves for different values of ρ_1—even for a fixed value of h_1—and similarly for each value of h_1 with ρ_1 fixed.

Using logarithm scale for eq.(3.2), the influence of ρ_1 and h_1 on the form of the curve may be removed as we get:

$$\log \bar{\rho} - \log \rho_1 = F(\log AB/2 - \log h_1) \tag{3.3}$$

or:

$$\log(\bar{\rho}/\rho_1) = \log F(\log AB/2h_1) \tag{3.4}$$

Eq.(3.4) shows that a plotting of $\bar{\rho}$ (ordinate) and $AB/2$ (abscissa) on a double-logarithm scale will give curves of exactly the same form for any value of ρ_1 and h_1 as long as ρ_2/ρ_1 remains constant. The effect, then, of ρ_1 is to shift the curve upward or downward parallel to the ordinate, and that of h_1 is to shift it to the left or right, parallel to the abscissa.

Thus, the form of the V.E.S. curves, plotted on a double-logarithm scale, is independent of the resistivity and thickness of the first layer in a two-layer section if ρ_2/ρ_1 is constant. This is found to be valid for a multi-layer geoelectric section also.

From field measurements we get apparent resistivity as a function of the electrode separation, i.e.; $\bar{\rho} = f(AB/2)$.

Using logarithm scale for this relation we get:

$$\log \bar{\rho} = F(\log AB/2) \tag{3.5}$$

Eq.(3.3) and (3.5) are of the form: $y - b = f(x - a)$, and: $y = f(x)$.

These equations are similar to each other, except that the first curve is shifted parallel to the coordinates with respect to the second curve plotted on logarithm scale. This shows that the interpretation of the field curves by matching is made possible through the use of the logarithmic scale. Thus, for each value of ρ_1 and h_1 we need not have different curves; a single master curve may be used for any value of ρ_1 and h_1, provided ρ_2/ρ_1 remains the same.

In Fig.9 the two-layer field curve ($\bar{\rho}$ vs. $AB/2$) is shown for $h_1 = 5$ m and $\rho_1 = 4$ Ωm and $\rho_2/\rho_1 = 7$. The two-layer theoretical master curve ($\bar{\rho}/\rho_1$ vs. $AB/2h_1$) for $\rho_2/\rho_1 = 7$ (the same as the field curve) is shown in the same diagram. These two curves can be matched easily by shifting the field curve over the theoretical curve, keeping the axes parallel. Actually, the theoretical curve can

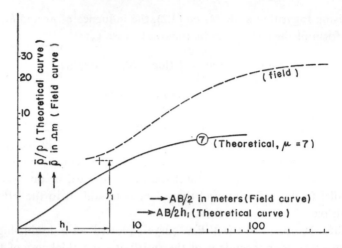

Fig.9. Relation between theoretical and field curves. Field curve of the same form as the theoretical one but shifted with respect to it and parallel to the coordinate axes.

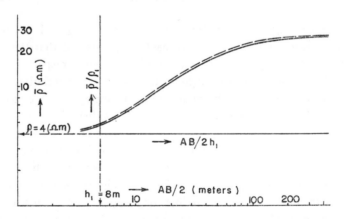

Fig.10. A two-layer field curve superimposed over a two-layer master curve. Origin of the master curve as read over the field curve gives the thickness and resistivity of the upper layer.

be matched with any field curve for any value of ρ_1 and h_1, provided ρ_2/ρ_1 is the same as that of the theoretical curve.

The method adopted for finding ρ_1 and h_1 has been indicated in Fig.10. The procedure is to plot the field curve on a transparent double-logarithm graph sheet which has a modulus the same as that for the theoretical master curves (a modulus of 62.5 mm), and then to superpose the transparent graph sheet on the master curve; the transparent graph sheet is moved parallel to the coordinates until a match is obtained. Fig.10 represents the matched condition, and the point on the transparent double-logarithm sheet coinciding with the origin of the master curve ($\bar{\rho}/\rho_1 = 1$, $AB/2h_1 = 1$) gives, along the abscissa, $\log(AB/2) = \log h_1$, i.e., $h_1 = AB/2$ m; and along the ordinate it gives $\log \bar{\rho} = \log \rho_1$, i.e., $\bar{\rho} = \rho_1 \ \Omega$m.

Thus, the use of the logarithm scale opens up the possibility of determining ρ_1 and h_1 from theoretical and field curves.

It is easily seen that on a double-logarithm scale, the conditions of limiting values are still satisfied and the asymptotic nature is retained.

Let us now find the asymptotic value of the apparent resistivity, when the second layer is of infinite resistivity (basement). It is obvious that at sufficiently large distances from the source, the current lines will be all parallel to the surface; and the equipotential surfaces will be cylindrical, having the vertical through the source as the axis. Let us consider an equipotential surface at a large distance r; then the current, I, is given by: $I = 2\pi r h_1 \cdot J$, where $J = E/\rho_1$. Therefore: $E = \rho_1 I/2\pi r h_1$.

Hence, the apparent resistivity for Schlumberger configuration is given by:

$$\bar{\rho} = 2\pi r^2 \cdot (E/I) = (\rho_1/h_1)r$$

Now taking the logarithm, we get:

$$\log \bar{\rho} = \log r + \log(\rho_1/h_1)$$
$$= \log r - \log(h_1/\rho_1) \qquad (3.6)$$

This is the equation of a straight line inclined at an angle of 45° to the abscissa, cutting it at a distance (h_1/ρ_1) from the origin. It will be shown later that for an n-layer earth (n-th layer of infinite resistivity) the same asymptotic relation holds good, provided ρ_1 is changed to ρ_s—longitudinal resistivity of $(n - 1)$ layers—and h_1 is changed to H—the total thickness of $(n - 1)$ layers.

PRINCIPLE OF REDUCTION OF TWO LAYERS

Consider a prism of unit cross-section, with thickness h and resistivity ρ. Then the resistance (T) normal to the face of the prism, and the conductance (S) parallel to the face of the prism, are given by:

$$T = h\rho \tag{3.7a}$$

and:

$$S = h/\rho \tag{3.7b}$$

wherefrom we get:

$$h = \sqrt{ST} \text{ and } \rho = \sqrt{T/S} \tag{3.8}$$

Thus, each value of S and T determines a section with definite values of h and ρ given by eq.(3.8). Now, from eq.(3.7a) we can write:

$$\log \rho = -\log h + \log T \tag{3.9}$$

This equation defines a straight line inclined at an angle of 135° to the h-axis and cutting it at a distance T from the origin, if ρ is plotted against h on a double-logarithm scale.

Similarly, from relation (3.7b) we get:

$$\log \rho = \log h - \log S \tag{3.10}$$

which defines a straight line —also see eq.(3.6)— inclined at an angle of 45° with the abscissa (h-axis) and meeting it at a distance S from the origin.

The point of intersection of the two straight lines defined by eq.(3.9) and (3.10) then uniquely defines the resistivity and thickness for a particular combination of T and S.

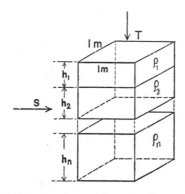

Fig.11. An n-layer prism of unit cross-section.

Consider now that the prism consists of n parallel homogeneous and isotropic layers of resistivities $\rho_1, \rho_2, \ldots \rho_n$ and thicknesses $h_1, h_2 \ldots h_n$, respectively (Fig.11).

When the current is flowing normal to the base, the total resistance of the prism is:

$$T = T_1 + T_2 + \ldots + T_n = \sum_{i=1}^{n} T_i$$

$$= \rho_1 h_1 + \rho_2 h_2 + \ldots + \rho_n h_n = \sum_{i=1}^{n} \rho_i h_i \qquad (3.11)$$

When the current is flowing parallel to the base, the total conductance is:

$$S = S_1 + S_2 + \ldots + S_n = \sum_{i=1}^{n} S_i$$

$$= h_1/\rho_1 + h_2/\rho_2 + \ldots + h_n/\rho_n = \sum_{i=1}^{n} h_i/\rho_i \qquad (3.12)$$

The parameters T and S defined as transverse resistance and longitudinal conductance, respectively, play a very important role in the interpretation of sounding data. It may be mentioned that MAILLET (1947) used the notations R and C for these parameters, and called them "Dar Zarrouk variable" and "Dar Zarrouk function", respectively.

For the particular case of a two-layer prism, we get:

$$T = T_1 + T_2 = \rho_1 h_1 + \rho_2 h_2 \tag{3.13}$$

and:

$$S = S_1 + S_2 = h_1/\rho_1 + h_2/\rho_2 \tag{3.14}$$

If ρ_s and ρ_t are, respectively, the longitudinal and transverse resistivities of the block, then:

$$\rho_t(h_1 + h_2) = \rho_1 h_1 + \rho_2 h_2 \tag{3.15}$$

and:

$$(h_1 + h_2)/\rho_s = h_1/\rho_1 + h_2/\rho_2 \tag{3.16}$$

Thus, the coefficient of anisotropy λ and the mean resistivity are, respectively, given by:

$$\lambda = \sqrt{\rho_t/\rho_s} = \frac{1}{h_1 + h_2}\{(\rho_1 h_1 + \rho_2 h_2)(h_1/\rho_1 + h_2/\rho_2)\}^{\frac{1}{2}} \tag{3.17}$$

and:

$$\rho_m = \left\{ \frac{h_1\rho_1 + h_2\rho_2}{h_1/\rho_1 + h_2/\rho_2} \right\}^{\frac{1}{2}} \tag{3.18}$$

We shall now assume that the anisotropic prism may be replaced by a homogeneous and isotropic prism of thickness h_e and resistivity ρ_e, which may be called, respectively, the effective thickness and the effective resistivity of the block.

Then:

$$\rho_e h_e = T = \rho_1 h_1 + \rho_2 h_2 \tag{3.19}$$

and:

$$h_e/\rho_e = S = h_1/\rho_1 + h_2/\rho_2 \tag{3.20}$$

from which we get:

$$h_e = \{(h_1\rho_1 + h_2\rho_2)(h_1/\rho_1 + h_2/\rho_2)\}^{\frac{1}{2}}$$
$$= \lambda(h_1 + h_2) = \lambda H \tag{3.21}$$

and:

$$\rho_e = \left\{ \frac{h_1\rho_1 + h_2\rho_2}{h_1/\rho_1 + h_2/\rho_2} \right\}^{\frac{1}{2}}$$
$$= \rho_m = \lambda\rho_s \tag{3.22}$$

Thus, it is possible to transform an isolated two-layer block (each homogeneous and isotropic) into a single homogeneous and isotropic medium. A complete isolation of this kind is possible in the case of A-type curves, where the third layer is highly resistive and the second layer is more resistive than the first. Here the effective thickness of the reduced layer is equal to λ times the total thickness, and the effective resistivity is equal to the mean resistivity of the mediums. Since λ is always greater than unity, the effective thickness of the composite layer is greater than the total thickness of the two layers. As explained in the next section, the effective thicknesses and resistivities of the reduced layers will be controlled by the subsurface resistivity distribution characteristic of the type curve.

PRINCIPLE OF REDUCTION OF A THREE-LAYER EARTH

We shall now consider the case of a three-layer earth. The left-hand part of the sounding curve in this case coincides with a two-layer curve having a parameter $\mu = \rho_2/\rho_1$; the closer the coincidence, the smaller the value of the spread AB. For larger values of AB, the right-hand part of the curve may be taken to coincide with a two-layer curve having a parameter $\mu_e = \rho_3/\rho_e$, where ρ_3 is the resistivity of the third layer and ρ_e some effective resistivity of a homogeneous layer replacing the first two layers. Our problem now is to find the parameters (the effective resistivity and effective thickness) of this reduced layer. From a careful study of a large number of theoretical, experimental and field curves, it has been possible to obtain some empirical laws for determining these parameters. These laws are different for the four different types of the three-layer curves and have been found to be very useful in the construction and interpretation of field curves.

These cases will now be considered separately.

Case I: H-type

In this case, the resistivity of the intermediate layer is lower than that of the top and the bottom layers. When the resistivity of the bottom layer is large, the sounding curve is appreciably affected by the resistive substratum for large values of AB, and the flow of current in the upper layers will be approximately parallel to the horizontal strata. Thus, in this case, the transverse resistance (T) is negligible; and the longitudinal conductance (S) is the sum of the longitudinal conductances of the top two layers.

Hence, if we replace the two upper layers by a single homogeneous layer with effective thickness h_H and effective resistivity ρ_H, it is easily seen that they are given by:

$$h_H = h_1 + h_2 \qquad (3.23)$$

and:

$$\rho_E = \frac{h_1 + h_2}{S_1 + S_2} = (h_1 + h_2)/(h_1/\rho_1 + h_2/\rho_2) = \rho_s \qquad (3.24)$$

These are sometimes known as Hummel's parameters.

On double-logarithm paper, the first eq.(3.23) represents a straight line parallel to the ordinate; the second eq.(3.24) represents a straight line inclined at an angle of 45° to the x-axis, cutting it at $S_1 + S_2$. The point of intersection of these two straight lines is known as Hummel point H, the coordinates (x_H, y_H) of which determine ρ_H and h_H.

Eq.(3.23) and (3.24) are utilized to plot auxiliary H-point charts for a large number of values of $\mu_2 = \rho_2/\rho_1$ and different values of $\nu_2 = h_2/h_1$ with:

$$\text{abscissa} = x_H/h_1 = 1 + \nu_2$$

and:

$$\text{ordinate} = y_H/\rho_1 = \frac{1 + \nu_2}{1 + \nu_2/\mu_2}$$

These auxiliary point charts (H) have been presented in Plate III, which can be directly used to find the H-point (i.e., ρ_H and h_H). The conditions for which the H-point charts have been plotted are strictly valid only for $\rho_3 = \infty$. It is, however, found that the charts can be used even for any arbitrary value of ρ_3 sufficiently greater than ρ_2. This forms the basis of a simple method of construction of empirical curves of the H-type.

Case II: A-type

In this case, the intermediate layer is more resistive than the first (i.e., $\rho_2 > \rho_1$). Hence, the effect of the transverse resistance T cannot be neglected. Also, since $\rho_3 > \rho_2$, we have additionally to take into account the longitudinal conductance S. Therefore, the T and S values of the reduced homogeneous layer will be the sum of those of the top two layers, i.e.:

$$T = T_1 + T_2 = h_1\rho_1 + h_2\rho_2$$

and:

$$S = S_1 + S_2 = h_1/\rho_1 + h_2/\rho_2$$

This case has already been dealt with, and the effective thickness and resistivity are given by—see eq.(3.21) and (3.22):

$$h_A = \sqrt{TS} = \lambda(h_1 + h_2) = \lambda H \tag{3.25}$$

and:

$$\rho_A = \sqrt{T/S} = \rho_m = \lambda\rho_s \tag{3.26}$$

These points are obviously the coordinates of the point of inter-section of the T and S lines (Fig.12). This point A may be called the "anisotropy point". Thus, the thickness of the reduced layer equivalent to the first two layers is not equal to the sum of the thicknesses (as in case I, i.e., H-type), but is λ times that. The resistivity of the reduced layer is also λ times the longitudinal resistivity of the first two layers.

As in case I, here also eq.(3.25) and (3.26) can be utilized to plot the auxiliary point charts (A) for various values of μ_2 and ν_2. These relations (3.25) and (3.26) may be rewritten as:

$$\begin{aligned}
\frac{x_A}{h_1} &= \{(1 + \nu_2/\mu_2)(1 + \nu_2\mu_2)\}^{\frac{1}{2}} \\
\frac{y_A}{\rho_1} &= \left\{\frac{1 + \nu_2\mu_2}{1 + (\nu_2/\mu_2)}\right\}^{\frac{1}{2}}
\end{aligned} \tag{3.27}$$

The values obtained from (3.27) are plotted in a similar manner as in case I, and have been presented in Plate III along with H-point charts. The coordinates of the point A (h_A and ρ_A) can either be

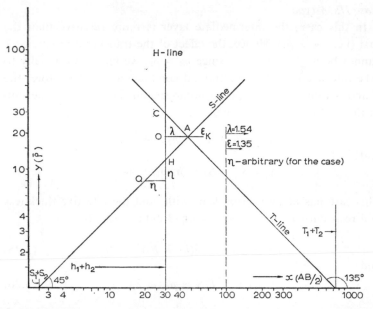

Fig.12. Triangle of anisotropy. Positions of *A*-, *K*- and *Q*-points with respect to *H*-point shown for a particular case: $\rho_1 = 5\ \Omega m$, $\rho_2 = 40\ \Omega m$, $h_1 = 10$ m, $h_2 = 20$ m, η - arbitrary.

calculated, using the above relations (3.27), or can be read from the curves available (Plate III).

Case III: K-type (modified A-type)

In this case, the resistivity of the intermediate layer is higher than that of the top and the bottom layers. The current flow in the upper two layers will be somewhat similar to case II, i.e., A-type, especially at smaller *AB*. Therefore both *T* and *S* should be considered. In this case, however, the intermediate layer being underlain by a less resistive layer, the lines of current flow within the second layer should have a larger vertical component than that of A-type. Hence, the conditions should be somewhat different than those of A-type section.

From an examination of the theoretical curves it is found that, in this case, the resistivity of the reduced layer remains the same

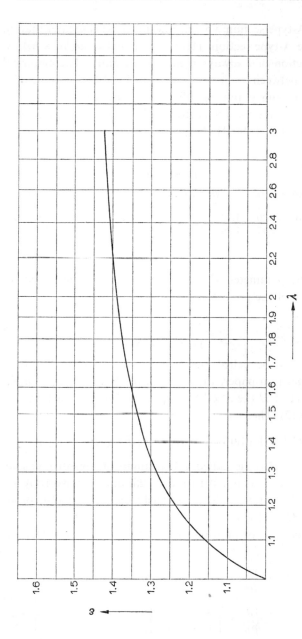

Fig.13. Variation of the factor ε with coefficient of anisotropy (λ).

as in the A-type section whereas its thickness is greater than in the case of the A-type section. Here h_K is equal to $\varepsilon\lambda(h_1 + h_2)$, where ε is a function of λ always greater than unity. The empirical relationship between λ and ε is shown in Fig.13. The value of ε can be read from this graph for different values of λ.

The values of λ and the corresponding values of ε may be tabulated as given in Table II (KALENOV, 1957).

TABLE II

VARIATION OF ε WITH COEFFICIENT OF ANISOTROPY

λ	1.10	1.20	1.30	1.40	1.50	1.70	2.00	2.50	3.00
ε	1.17	1.17	1.29	1.32	1.33	1.36	1.38	1.40	1.42

Thus, the parameter of the reduced layer is determined by the coordinates of the point K, given by:

$$x_K = \varepsilon\sqrt{TS}$$
$$y_K = \sqrt{T/S} \qquad (3.28)$$

Point K may be called the "displaced anisotropy" point. On double-logarithm paper, the abscissa of A is $\log[\lambda(h_1 + h_2)]$, and the abscissa of H (i.e., "O") is $\log(h_1 + h_2)$, as shown in the diagram (Fig.12). Then:

$$OA = \log\{\lambda(h_1 + h_2)\} - \log(h_1 + h_2) = \log\lambda$$

The triangle HAC is called the triangle of anisotropy, and the height (OA) of it is equal to the coefficient of anisotropy λ. The location of point K is then obviously on the line OA, produced such that $AK = \log\varepsilon$.

The equations for plotting the auxiliary point chart (K) may be written as:

$$\frac{x_K}{h_1} = \varepsilon\{(1 + v_2/\mu_2)(1 + v_2\mu_2)\}^{\frac{1}{2}}$$

$$\frac{y_K}{\rho_1} = \left\{\frac{1 + v_2\mu_2}{1 + v_2/\mu_2}\right\}^{\frac{1}{2}} \qquad (3.29)$$

The curves for various values of v_2 and μ_2 have been presented in Plate IV and the K-point can be located either with the help of these charts or from the above relations (3.29).

Case IV: Q-type (modified H-type)

In this case, the resistivity of the intermediate layer is less than that of the top layer. Hence, the initial part of the sounding curves resembles that of H-type sections; but auxiliary H-point charts cannot be used, as the Q-type is underlain by a less resistive layer.

In this case, it is found empirically that the total thickness of the reduced layer is less than $(h_1 + h_2)$ by a factor η, depending on the values of μ_2 and v_2 of the electrical section. The value of η can be read from the curves given in Fig.14, plotted for various values of μ_2 and v_2.

The effective resistivity of the reduced layer is also taken as less than the mean longitudinal resistivity by the same factor η. Then the coordinates of Q are given by:

$$x_Q = \frac{H}{\eta}$$
$$y_Q = \frac{1}{\eta} \frac{H}{S} \hspace{2cm} (3.30)$$

It is easily seen that point Q (Fig.12) is graphically found by decreasing η times the coordinates of H. The location of the Q-point with reference to the H-point has been shown in the "triangle of anisotropy" diagram (Fig.12) for a specific value of η.

The set of equations (3.30) may be rewritten to plot the auxiliary point charts (Q) for various values of μ_2 and v_2 as:

$$\frac{x_Q}{h_1} = \frac{1}{\eta} (1 + v_2)$$
$$\frac{y_Q}{\rho_1} = \frac{1}{\eta} \frac{1 + v_2}{1 + (v_2/\mu_2)} \hspace{2cm} (3.31)$$

The Q-point may be taken from the charts (Plate IV) or calculated from these relations (3.31) with the help of Fig.14.

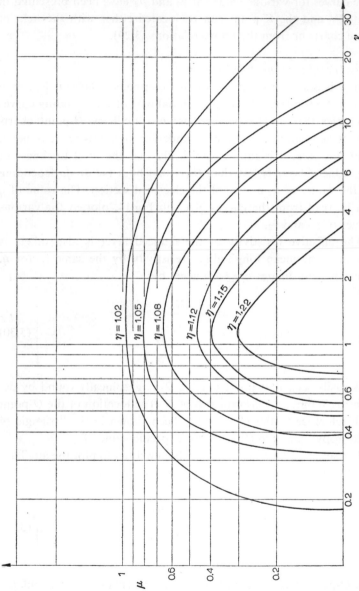

Fig.14. Dependance of the empirical relation between v and μ on factor η.

USE OF THE PRINCIPLE OF EQUIVALENCE

It has been mentioned earlier (Chapter 2) that for certain relations of the parameters of a three-layer section, changes in resistivity and thickness of the intermediate layer do not produce any noticeable changes in the form of the sounding curve. In such cases it is not possible to distinguish between two different intermediate layers, and error may be involved in the interpretation of such sections.

Thus, for sections of the H- or A-type, it is found that the form of the curve remains practically the same if within certain limits the values of h_2 and ρ_2 are multiplied by the same factor. In other words, H- or A-type sections are practically equivalent within certain limits if $h_2/\rho_2 = S_2$ remains the same. These sections may be called equivalent with respect to S.

Also, for sections of K- or Q-type, the form of the curves does not change appreciably if h_2 is increased or decreased by a certain factor and ρ_2 is correspondingly decreased or increased by the same factor. Thus, if $h_2\rho_2 = T_2$ remains constant, any change of h_2 and ρ_2 separately does not produce any noticeable change in the form of the curve. Such sections may be called equivalent with respect to T.

The mathematical proof of this principle has been given in Chapter 2 under certain conditions of thickness and resistivity of the intermediate layer. Let us examine a few examples of equivalent curves of the four types.

(a) H-type; $\rho_3 = \infty$. In this case, the curve $h_2/h_1 = 1$; $\rho_2/\rho_1 = 1/19$, i.e., $S_2/S_1 = 19$, is almost equivalent to the curve given by: $h_2/h_1 = 2$; $\rho_2/\rho_1 = 1/9$, i.e., $S_2/S_1 = 18$ (refer to sets of charts 84s and 85s in COMPAGNIE GÉNÉRALE DE GÉOPHYSIQUE, 1955, 1963).

(b) A-type; $\rho_3 = \infty$. Here the equivalent curves are given by:
$v_2 = 2$; $\mu_2 = 39$, i.e., $S_2/S_1 = 1/19.5$ (refer to set 96s)
and:
$v_2 = 1$; $\mu_2 = 19$, i.e., $S_2/S_1 = 1/19$ (refer to set 97s)

(c) K-type; $\rho_3 = 0$. The equivalent sets are given by:
$v_2 = 2$; $\mu_2 = 19$; $T_2/T_1 = 38$ (refer to set 91s)

and:
$$\nu_2 = 1; \quad \mu_2 = 39; \quad T_2/T_1 = 39 \quad \text{(refer to set 92s)}$$
(d) Q-type; $\rho_3 = 0$.
$$\nu_2 = 2; \quad \mu_2 = 1/39; \quad T_2/T_1 = 1/19.5 \quad \text{(refer to set 80s)}$$
and:
$$\nu_2 = 1; \quad \mu_2 = 1/19; \quad T_2/T_1 = 1/19 \quad \text{(refer to set 79s)}$$
are the equivalent curves.

The principle of equivalence, as shown above, applies only for small values of $\nu_2 = h_2/h_1$. The ratio may be different for different values of $\mu_2 = \rho_2/\rho_1$ and $\mu_3 = \rho_3/\rho_1$. For interpretation of sounding data it is thus important to know the maximum values of h_2/h_1 beyond which the principle of equivalence does not hold good

TABLE III

TABLE OF LIMITING VALUES FOR ν_2 AND μ_2 WITH RESPECT TO S AND T

Equivalent with respect to S			*Equivalent with respect to T*		
Maximum value of ν_2 for which μ_2 and ν_2 can be decreased without limit	Maximum possible value of factor of increase of ν_2 and μ_2		Maximum value of ν_2 for which μ_2 can be increased and ν_2 decreased without limit	Maximum possible factor of decrease of μ_2 and increase of ν_2	
H-type ($\rho_3 = \rho_1$)			*K-type* ($\rho_3 = \rho_1$)		
μ_2	ν_2		μ_2	ν_2	
1/39	2	1.6	39	9	1.7
1/19	1	1.6	19	5	1.6
1/9	1	1.6	9	2	1.6
1/4	1/2	1.4	4	1/2	1.5
3/7	1/3	1.4	7/3	1/2	1.5
2/3	1/5	1.4	3/2	1/3	1.5
A-type ($\rho_3 = \infty$)			*Q-type* ($\rho_3 = 0$)		
39	3	without limit	1/39	—	—
19	2	-do-	1/19	1/3	2.6–2.3
9	1	3.8	1/9	1/3	2.2–2.1
4	1	2.5	1/4	1/3	1.9–1.9
7/3	1	1.7	3/7	1/3	1.8–1.8
3/2	1	1.5	2/3	1/3	1.5–1.5

(Table III). Besides, for interpretation of field curves, it is of great practical importance to know the limits within which h_2 and ρ_2 may be varied, satisfying the equivalence of the curves.

Assuming that the error in field measurements is 5%, we may say that the curves having deviation less than 5% cannot be differentiated from each other. Let us consider, for example, the theoretical curves of the K-type having constant T_2/T_1, $\rho_3 = 0$ and variables h_2/h_1 and ρ_2/ρ_1. It is seen that for $\rho_2/\rho_1 > 9$, the curves are equivalent within 5%. In other words, curves for $\rho_2/\rho_1 = 9$, 19 and 39 practically coincide and may be taken as the same as for $\rho_2/\rho_1 = \infty$ and $T_2/T_1 = h_2\rho_2/h_1\rho_1 = 12$. Thus, if $\rho_2/\rho_1 = 9$, then starting with $h_2/h_1 = 1.3$, we can increase ρ_2/ρ_1 and correspondingly decrease h_2/h_1 without limit and shall not notice much difference in the nature of the curves. If $\rho_2/\rho_1 = 19$, the maximum limit of h_2/h_1 will be 0.6, and so on.

The problem of equivalence has been discussed in detail by PYLAEV (1948). He has given nomograms for all four types of three-layer sections, which give the limiting values of ρ_2 and h_2 for the principle to be valid. The nomograms have been presented in Plate V–VII. From these nomograms we can find the numerical values of the limits of applicability of the principle of equivalence for different types of sections. Some numerical values of the maximum limits of equivalence are given in Table III.

It is found that the region of equivalence in the case of Q-type section is considerably less than that in the cases of A-, K- and H-type sections.

Pylaev's nomograms

Pylaev's nomograms for determining the limits of v_2 and μ_2 are plotted with $\mu_2 = \rho_2/\rho_1$ on the abscissa and $v_2 = h_2/h_1$ on the ordinate, and these are of four types (H, A, K and Q), as presented in Plate V–VIII. Solid lines indicate the limiting values of μ_2 and v_2 for equivalence, and the dashed lines are lines of equal S_2/S_1 (for H and A) and equal T_2/T_1 (for K and Q).

The use of the curves for H-type (Plate V) has been shown in the nomogram itself. The procedure is given below:

(*1*) Plot the point μ_2 and ν_2 of the given case in the nomogram (Plate V).

(*2*) Draw through this point a line parallel to the dashed lines (lines of equal S_2/S_1) until it touches the solid lines on either side but with different slopes.

(*3*) Draw a rectangle with this line in (*2*) as the diagonal. This rectangle gives the limiting values of ν_2 and μ_2 for equivalence in the required case.

An example for the limiting values for $\mu_2 = 1/39$ and $\nu_2 = 3$ has been shown in Plate V where the shaded rectangle gives the limits of equivalence. The limits of equivalence for this case lies between $\nu_2 = 1.6$ and 4.4, and $\mu_2 = 0.018$ and 0.036. The procedure is similar in the cases of A-, K- and Q-types of equivalent curves.

The principle of equivalence plays an important role in the graphical construction of field curves as well as in their interpretation. Suppose, for example, it is necessary to find an H-type curve with parameters $\mu_2 = 1/30$, $\nu_2 = 4$, and $\rho_3 = \infty$. A theoretical curve with such parameters does not exist in the sets of master curves published. The closest theoretical curve has the value $\mu_2 = 1/39$. Pylaev's nomogram shows that for the given parameters, μ_2 may be changed within the limits of equivalence. Thus, the corresponding value of ν_2 is given by $\nu_2/\mu_2 = 120 = \nu_2'/\mu_2'$, i.e., $\nu_2' = 120/39 = 3.1$. Thus, we can use the curve $\mu_2 = 1/39$, $\nu_2 = 3$, $\rho_3 = \infty$, which is equivalent to the given section within an error of about 5%. To get a K-type curve, equivalent with respect to T, for the values $\mu_2 = 30$, $\nu_2 = 4$ and $\rho_3 = 0$ we can use the relation $\nu_2' = \mu_2\nu_2/\mu_2'$ and $\mu_2' = \mu_2\nu_2/\nu_2'$. Then the parameters of the new curve equivalent to the given K-type section are: $\mu_2 = 39$, $\nu_2 = 3$ and $\rho_3 = 0$.

It should be remembered that for Q-type and A-type sections the procedure is exactly the same as for those of K- and H-types, respectively.

GRAPHICAL CONSTRUCTION OF EMPIRICAL CURVES

Construction of two-layer curves

If a two-layer curve for ρ_2/ρ_1, other than the values for which the curves are available in published form, is required, it can be plotted with sufficient accuracy by graphical interpolation. The following procedure may be adopted:

(1) Draw vertical lines perpendicular to the abscissa (in Plate I and II), the intersection of which with the master curves gives the various values of ρ_2/ρ_1 and corresponding $\bar{\rho}/\rho_1$ for a certain fixed value of $AB/2h_1$.

(2) Plot along the ordinate the values of $\bar{\rho}/\rho_1$ and the corresponding values of ρ_2/ρ_1 along the abscissa for a fixed value of $AB/2h_1$. There will be as many curves as the number of $AB/2h_1$ values taken.

(3) Read out the values of $\bar{\rho}/\rho_1$ corresponding to the required value of ρ_2/ρ_1 for various values of $AB/2h_1$, and tabulate.

(4) Plot the values $AB/2h_1$ along the abscissa and the corresponding values of $\bar{\rho}/\rho_1$ along the ordinate, and then draw a smooth curve passing through these points.

This gives the two-layer master curve for the required intermediate values of ρ_2/ρ_1, i.e., other than those available in charts 1s (COMPAGNIE GÉNÉRALE DE GÉOPHYSIQUE, 1963; ANONYMOUS, 1963a).

Construction of three-layer curves

The two-layer theoretical master curves (Plate I, II), the auxiliary point charts (Plate III, IV) along with the albums of three-layer and four-layer curves (COMPAGNIE GÉNÉRALE DE GÉOPHYSIQUE, 1955, 1963; ANONYMOUS, 1963a, b) may help in the empirical construction of multi-layer curves for values of the parameters for which theoretical curves are not available.

The following steps are recommended for the construction of three-layer field curves of the H-type:

(1) Plot on a double-logarithm, transparent graph sheet with a modulus of 62.5 mm the point with coordinates h_1 and ρ_1.

(2) Superpose this point on the origin of a two-layer theoretical master curve such that the axes are parallel.

(3) Draw the curve with $\mu_2 = \rho_2/\rho_1$, and the left-hand part of the three-layer curve is obtained. Use interpolation, if necessary, as explained above in the case of two-layer curves.

(4) Locate point H, given by the point h_H and ρ_H, from the sets of eq.(3.23) and(3.24) or from the auxiliary point charts (Plate III).

(5) Now put point H on the origin of the set of two-layer master curves and draw the curve corresponding to $\mu = \rho_3/\rho_H$. This forms the right-hand part of the curve.

(6) Connect the left-hand curve with the right-hand one with a smooth curve to get the intermediate portion. In order to find more accurately the transitional portion of the curve, use is often made of the theoretical three-layer curves having $\mu = \rho_2/\rho_1$ and a value of ρ_3 nearer to the given value. Put the point (h_1, ρ_1) on the origin of such a set of three-layer curves and draw the transitional part by interpolation (for details refer to the examples at the end of this chapter).

Sometimes, for plotting the intermediate part, use is made of the "principle of equivalence" to choose the proper set of curve. The application of this principle has been discussed in the previous section and the theory dealt with in Chapter 2. In order to plot three-layer master curves instead of the field curves discussed just now, the first step is slightly modified, as explained in example 2, at the end of this chapter.

The procedure for graphical construction of three-layer A-, K- and Q-type curves is exactly the same as that already explained for the H-type. The respective A-, K- and Q-points, instead of the H-point, are to be determined, depending on the type of curve to be constructed.

Construction of four-layer curves

It is found that, under suitable conditions, the principle of reduction and the method of graphical construction as explained above can be extended to multi-layer cases also.

The procedure for graphical construction of four-layer field curves is similar to that for the three-layer ones explained above. Here, use is made of the two- and three-layer master curves, and the following steps may be adopted:

(*1*) Plot the point (h_1, ρ_1) on a transparent double-logarithm graph sheet with a modulus of 62.5 mm.

(*2*) Superpose this point on the origin of a set of three-layer master curves decided by the values $(h_1, \rho_1, h_2, \rho_2$ and $\rho_3)$ and draw the curve for $\nu_2 = h_2/h_1$. If the curve for the required value $\mu_2 = \rho_2/\rho_1$ is not available, use the principle of equivalence and choose the nearest value. If the principle of equivalence does not help, then construct the required three-layer curve with the help of two-layer master curves as explained above.

(*3*) Find the values of ρ_{e1} and h_{e1}, i.e., the effective resistivity and the thickness of the first two top layers, either from the auxiliary point charts or calculate them from the given relations (as explained earlier in a discussion of reduction) for the type section (H, A, K or Q) formed by the first, second and the third layers.

(*4*) Now, with the (h_{e1}, ρ_{e1}) point as the origin, plot a three-layer master curve for the values ρ_{e1}, h_{e1}, ρ_3, h_3, ρ_4. Use of the principle of equivalence may be made if necessary, as in step (*2*).

(*5*) Again, the effective resistivity and thickness of the reduced layer are obtained by combining ρ_{e1}, h_{e1} and ρ_3, h_3, using the corresponding relations or charts. This gives ρ_{e2} and h_{e2}.

6) The point (h_{e2}, ρ_{e2}) is then plotted on the transparent double-logarithm graph sheet and placed on the origin of the two-layer master curves.

(*7*) Draw the two-layer curve for the value of $\mu = \rho_4/\rho_{e2}$.

(*8*) Join the intermediate parts by suitable smoothing technique with the help of the four-layer curves available in ANONYMOUS, 1963b (refer to examples at the end of this chapter).

QUALITATIVE INTERPRETATION

The aim of geophysical interpretation of resistivity sounding data is to determine the thickness and resistivity of different horizons from a study of the V.E.S. field curves and to use these results to obtain a complete geological picture of the area under investigation.

It is sometimes useful to make a rapid qualitative study of the field curves before a detailed quantitative interpretation of the same is undertaken. Several quantitative methods of interpretation have been used by different workers (KALENOV, 1957) under different geological conditions. In this section, we shall describe a method particularly useful for mapping the basement of high resistivity. The method depends on the determination of the total longitudinal conductance (S) of the geoelectric section from the right-hand asymptotic part of the sounding curve.

It was shown earlier that the asymptotic part of the sounding curve is a straight line, inclined at an angle of 45°, when the basement is of infinite resistivity. It was also proved —see eq.(3.10)— that the intersection of this straight line with the abscissa (i.e., $AB/2$) at $\bar{\rho} = 1$, gives the value of the total longitudinal conductance of the section:

$$S = S_1 + S_2 + \ldots = \frac{h_1 + h_2 + \ldots}{\rho_s} = \frac{H}{\rho_s}$$

where ρ_s is the longitudinal resistivity of the whole section.

Two-layer earth

In the case of a two-layer earth with a basement complex of a high resistivity ($\rho_2 = \infty$), the problem is simplified. Here the value of $\bar{\rho}$ for small AB (i.e., $AB \to 0$) gives ρ_1; and the value of S is read from the asymptotic part, giving the value of the depth of the basement, i.e., $h_1 = \rho_1 S$.

In case of a finely layered thick sedimentary section underlain by a basement, the depth obtained from the S value and the resistivity of the surface layers may not give the true depth of the basement because of the anisotropy. In this case, the depth is given by $h = \rho_s S$.

Here it is necessary to find ρ_s from some independent measurements of the true depth (e.g., by actual drilling or from geophysical well-logging) at a few places where sounding curves are available. It is found that ρ_s does not change appreciably in an area for small lateral variations of the resistivity and thickness of the sedimentary section.

Thus, knowing the value of ρ_s at a few control points, it is possible to map the basement from the S-part of the sounding curves only. Obviously, this procedure may be adopted for basement mapping in a multi-layer section, provided the assumption of a small variation in ρ_s in the area under consideration is approximately valid. Thus, under favourable conditions it is possible to obtain a rapid qualitative idea of the depth of basement in an area through the study of the S-part of the curve.

Three-layer earth

In the interpretation of three-layer H- and A-type field curves only ($\rho_3 = \infty$), the following steps may be followed. Only two-layer master curves need be used:

(1) On matching the left-hand part of the curve with the two-layer master curves, the values of ρ_1 and h_1 are obtained.

(2) The value of S is read from the intersection of the tangent to the asymptotic part of the field curve with the abscissa at $\bar{\rho} = 1$. In a three-layer case, $S = S_1 + S_2$, where $S_1 = (h_1/\rho_1)$ and S_2 is given by $S - (h_1/\rho_1) = h_2/\rho_2$.

(3) If ρ_2 is known from some independent measurements (e.g., electrical logs) at certain locations in the area, the thickness h_2 of the second layer is calculated by the relation $h_2 = S_2\rho_2$. Thus, we can get the depth of the basement $H = h_1 + h_2$.

The same procedure is followed for other points, and the basement can be mapped from a knowledge of ρ_2 and the use of two-layer master curves only. Detailed procedure for qualitative interpretation of three-layer sounding curves has been given in example 6 at the end of this chapter (cf. Fig. 21). This semi-quantitative method can be extended to a multi-layer sedimentary section underlain by a basement.

QUANTITATIVE INTERPRETATION

The problem of the quantitative interpretation of vertical electrical sounding is to determine the thickness of the different formations having different resistivities from the field sounding curves. The interpretation is based on comparing the field curves with the curves obtained theoretically, or constructed graphically, having suitably chosen parameters. In the case of perfect coincidence of the theoretical with the field curve (complete matching), the values of the field parameters are the same as those of the geoelectrical section for which the theoretical or graphical curves have been constructed. It is, however, practically impossible to have an album of theoretical master curves representing all geological situations met in the field. It is thus necessary to devise ways and means of interpreting the observed field curves with the help of a limited number of theoretical curves available in published form. The methods of computation of apparent resistivity curves (used for the comparison of field curves) from the resistivity stratification in the subsurface (FLATHE, 1955; VAN DAM, 1965) becomes impracticable in the field. Some efforts have been made to find a method for direct interpretation of sounding data, i.e., for determining the parameters of a geoelectric section from the surface measurement of apparent resistivity data (SLICHTER, 1933; BELLUIGI, 1956; KOEFOED, 1965). These methods have not been very successful from practical points of view, and hence will not be discussed.

In this section we shall describe the procedure for the interpretation of two-, three-, four- and multi-layer curves by using the theoretical master curves available and the "auxiliary point charts" and Pylaev's nomograms, as explained earlier. This analytic-graphical auxiliary point method of interpretation (EBERT, 1943; KALENOV, 1957) has been found quite useful from a practical point of view, and is being widely used by geophysicists engaged in geoelectric sounding.

Interpretation of two-layer curves

Two-layer V.E.S. field curves may be of two types: (1) $\rho_2 > \rho_1$

and (2) $\rho_2 < \rho_1$. The following procedure may be adopted for interpretation:

(a) Plot the field curve on a double-logarithm transparent graph sheet with a modulus of 62.5 mm, with $\bar{\rho}$ on the ordinate and $AB/2$ along the abscissa.

(b) Superpose the field curve on the sets of two-layer master curves, Plate I for case (1) and Plate II for case (2), and shift the curve, keeping the axes parallel to the coordinate system until a good match is obtained.

The coordinates of the origin of the master curves as read on the field curve (Fig.10) gives the values of ρ_1 and h_1. The value of $\mu_2 = \rho_2/\rho_1$ is read from the theoretical curve, and ρ_2 calculated. It should be remembered that for a finely layered sedimentary section, ρ_1 and ρ_2 represent the mean resistivities of the top and the bottom layers. If no match is obtained, interpolation on logarithm scale is necessary. In the case of a highly resistive bottom layer, the simplified procedure explained in the section on qualitative interpretation may be adopted.

Interpretation of three-layer curves

Interpretation of three-layer vertical electrical sounding (V.E.S.) field curves can be achieved with the help of available two- and three-layer master curves (COMPAGNIE GÉNÉRALE DE GÉOPHYSIQUE, 1963, and ANONYMOUS, 1963a) and the auxiliary point charts (Plate III and IV).

For interpretation of three-layer field curves, the following procedure may be adopted:

(1) Plot the field curve on a transparent double-logarithm graph sheet with a modulus of 62.5 mm, and match the left-hand part of the curve by superposing the field curve on the set of two-layer master curves, keeping the axes parallel to the coordinates. The coordinates of the origin of the master curve, as read on the field curve, give ρ_1 and h_1. From the curve on which the match is obtained, and by interpolation if necessary, $\mu_2 = \rho_2/\rho_1$ can be read. Since ρ_1 is known, ρ_2 can be calculated.

(2) Matching of the curves with three-layer master curves will consist of the following steps:

(a) Choose the right set of three-layer master curves from the knowledge of ρ_1, $\mu_2 = (\rho_2/\rho_1)$, already noted in step (1) and the most probable value of ρ_3 (guessed at).

(b) Superpose the three-layer field curve with the point (h_1, ρ_1) on the origin of the three-layer master curve set chosen in step (2a), and read the value of $v_2(h_2/h_1)$ from the curve with which the field curve matches. To obtain v_2, interpolation on a logarithm scale may be done, if necessary. For actual interpolation and detailed procedure, refer to example 7 at the end of this chapter.

(c) If there is an exact match with a three-layer curve, the value of ρ_3 may also be read from the asymptotic value. Thus, so far we have obtained: ρ_1, h_1, μ_2 (hence ρ_2), v_2 and ρ_3, and the problem is then solved, since $h_2 = v_2 \times h_1$.

(3) If the value of ρ_3 cannot be obtained accurately, the following procedure—using the auxiliary point charts and two-layer master curves—is recommended.

(a) The field curve is superposed on the proper set of auxiliary point charts, with the point (h_1, ρ_1) on the origin of the chart.

(b) Read the corresponding values of $\mu_2(\rho_2/\rho_1)$ and $v_2(h_2/h_1)$, with the axes parallel. This gives h_e and ρ_e.

(c) Now put this point (h_e, ρ_e) on the origin of the two-layer master curves, and match the right-hand part with the suitable, two-layer curve, which gives ρ_3/ρ_e.

Since ρ_e is known in step (3b), ρ_3 is calculated. This gives a check on the value of ρ_3.

(4) The following procedure is recommended if the three-layer curve for requisite parameters is not available and the principle of equivalence is applicable.

(a) If the three-layer curve for the proper value of μ_2 is not obtained, the value nearest to it, i.e., μ_2', is taken.

(b) The value of v_2' is then obtained, after matching with the three-layer curves.

(c) The actual value v_2 is obtained by the principles of equivalence, i.e., by keeping S_2/S_1 (for H- and A-types) and T_2/T_1 (for K- and Q-types) constant.

For H- and A-type: $v_2/\mu_2 = v_2'/\mu_2'$, i.e., $v_2 = v_2'\mu_2/\mu_2'$.

For K- and Q-type: $v_2\mu_2 = v_2'\mu_2'$, i.e., $v_2 = v_2'\mu_2'/\mu_2$.

These are valid, provided the corresponding values are within the limits of equivalence as defined by Pylaev's nomograms (Plates V–VIII).

(5) When the three-layer master curves are not available and the principles of equivalence are not applicable, the following procedure—using two-layer master curves and "auxiliary point charts"—is recommended:

(a) Find the values of ρ_1, h_1 and ρ_2 from the two-layer master curves, as explained in step (1).

(b) Match the last part of the curve with a two-layer master curve. Put a cross-mark on the field curve, corresponding to the origin of the set of master curves. This gives ρ_e and h_e.

(c) Put the point (h_1, ρ_1) on the origin of the auxiliary point charts and read the value of v_2 corresponding to the cross-mark.

(d) From the knowledge of h_1, h_2 is obtained from v_2.

If the bottom layer is a highly resistive basement, we can adopt the simplified procedure for interpretation as explained in the section on qualitative interpretation.

Interpretation of four-layer curves

Interpretation of four-layer field curves consists of the following steps:

(1) With the help of two-layer master curves, as in the case of three-layer interpretation, the values of ρ_1, h_1 and μ_2 are obtained.

(2) Then, with the values of ρ_1, h_1 and μ_2 noted in step (1) and a suitable choice of ρ_3, the value of v_2 is obtained, as in the case of the three-layer curves.

(3) From the knowledge of ρ_1, h_1, ρ_2 and h_2, the resistivity and thickness of the reduced layer, i.e., ρ_{e1} and h_{e1}, are obtained with the analytical formulas for the type curves or from the auxiliary point charts for corresponding type curves.

(*4*) The whole curve now reduces to a three-layer curve, with parameters ρ_{e1}, h_{e1}, ρ_3, h_3 and ρ_4. The interpretation now is limited to a three-layer case, with the ρ_{e1}, h_{e1} point superposed on the origin of the three-layer theoretical master curves. The procedure for the rest of the curve is similar to that of a three-layer case.

Effect of dip on interpretation

We have so far discussed the apparent resistivity curves only for a horizontally layered earth, and the interpretation techniques explained in previous sections apply strictly when the boundaries between different layers are horizontal. Often, electrical sounding is carried out in regions where the boundaries of separation between different layers are inclined. It is necessary, therefore, to examine the effect of the inclination of beds on vertical electrical sounding curves.

The theoretical problem of potential distribution over a two-layer earth having an inclined boundary of separation has been discussed by AL'PIN (1940), TIKHONOV (1946), and later by UNZ (1953), MAEDA (1955) and DE GERY and KUNETZ (1956).

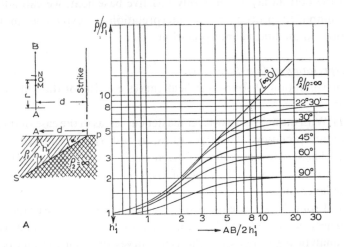

Fig.15. Effect of dip on Schlumberger curves. A. Expansion of electrodes parallel to strike. Lower layer highly resistive. B. Expansion of electrodes across the strike. d = distance of the sounding point from the contact.

AL'PIN (1940) published a set of 16 two-layer master curves for Schlumberger configuration parallel to the strike direction. These curves are no longer easily available. One such set of curves is reproduced in Fig.15A in which the apparent resistivity is plotted against $AB/2h_1'$, where h_1' is the depth perpendicular (not the vertical depth) to the boundary. The curves have been plotted for values

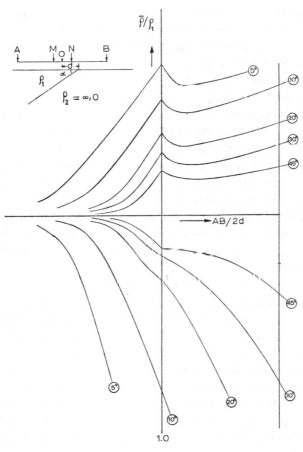

B

Fig.15B (Legend see p.74).

of the angle of inclination (dip) $\alpha = 0°$, $22°30'$, $30°$, $45°$, $60°$ and $90°$, with an infinite resistivity contrast (i.e., $\rho_2/\rho_1 = \infty$). Similar curves are also available for different values of the resistivity contrast. Recently a number of master curves (presented as NK-series) for inclined contacts with a spread of electrodes both parallel and perpendicular to the strike direction have been published (ANONYMOUS, 1963c). Two such sets of curves are given in Plate IX and Fig.15B. Curves for inclined contacts have been reproduced from the ANONYMOUS (1963c) album in English (AL′PIN et al., 1966).

From the curves in Plate IX it is seen that as the angle of inclination increases, the curves differ widely from each other—such that an increase in α raises the left-hand part of the curve and lowers the right-hand part. If the two-layer master curves for horizontal boundaries (Plate I, II) are used to interpret the sounding curves, for an inclined two-layer contact, considerable error is involved, particularly when α is large. For example, take the curve for $\alpha = \pi/4$ in Plate IX. If this curve is interpreted by means of Plate I, ignoring the dip, we get $\rho_2/\rho_1 \simeq 4$ and $h_1 = 0.4$ times the actual vertical depth below the sounding point. However, if the angle of inclination (α) is not more than 15–20°, the ordinary two-layer master curves may be used without appreciable error (less than 10%). If the basement must be surveyed when α is small, it is obvious that the Schlumberger sounding is unsuitable. In such a case, dipole sounding may be carried out. This is explained in Chapter 5.

In practice, if it is known beforehand that the boundary is inclined, then quantitative interpretation is possible when one of the parameters $(\alpha$ or $\rho_2/\rho_1)$ is known. Then, using the master curves for inclined contact, the other parameter and the depth of the bottom layer can be determined. In an unknown area, the dip of the bed can be detected by carrying out sounding at a point in two mutually perpendicular directions. If the strike direction is approximately known, the sounding should be done at several points, with a spread parallel to the strike direction and the depths computed from the two-layer master curves for horizontal layers (Plate I, II). Thus, the trace of the lower bed and the angle of inclination can be found. The interpretation is reasonably accurate for small dips. For larger dips, however, the master curves available (Plate IX) for dipping contacts should be used.

Besides the possibility of the effect of inclination of the beds on the interpretation of sounding curves, the following points should also be remembered at the interpretation stage:

(*1*) An attempt should be made to match with a three-layer master curve in the beginning, instead of a two-layer one, if such sets are available. This introduces a lesser amount of error.

(*2*) Geological knowledge of the area, especially with regard to possible subsurface formations, should be used to determine the curve type.

(*3*) Logging data at some selected points in the area should be used, if possible, as a guide for the interpretation.

(*4*) The whole set of sounding field curves for a given area should be studied simultaneously. This helps the interpreter to choose the most probable geological solution, and the interpretation is greatly improved.

EXAMPLES

Graphical construction of three-layer field and master curves

Example 1. Construct graphically the following three-layer H-type curve:

$$\rho_1 = 16 \, \Omega m; \quad \rho_2 = 4 \, \Omega m; \quad \rho_3 = 41 \, \Omega m$$
$$h_1 = \quad 3 \, m; \quad h_2 = 15 \, m; \quad h_3 = \infty$$

Since the field curve is plotted with the apparent resistivity along the ordinate and $AB/2$ on the abscissa, the starting point for the construction of the field curve will be (ρ_1, h_1) and not the origin (1, 1) of the master curves. The following steps may be adopted:

(*a*) Superpose the point (16, 3), plotted on a double-logarithm transparent graph sheet of proper modulus, on the origin of the two-layer master curve set.

(b) Plot the two-layer curve for $\mu_2 = \rho_2/\rho_1 = 4/16 = 1/4$, as shown in Fig.16A.

(c) Next, find the H-point by combining the top two layers. The coordinates of the H-point are obtained from the analytical formulas:

$$\rho_H = \frac{h_1 + h_2}{(h_1/\rho_1) + (h_2/\rho_2)} = 4.6 \ \Omega m$$

and:

$$h_H = h_1 + h_2 = 18 \ m$$

To find the H-point graphically, make the point (16, 3) coincide with the origin of the H-point charts (Plate III) and locate the H-point at the intersection of $v_2 = h_2/h_1 = 5$ and $\mu_2 = \rho_2/\rho_1 = 1/4$.

(d) With the H-point on the origin of the two-layer master curves, plot the curve for the resistivity ratio $\mu = \rho_3/\rho_H = 8.8 \simeq 9$.

(e) In order to interpolate the intermediate part of the curve, use is made of the three-layer master curves. For the present case, the three-layer curve is available for $v_2 = 5$ and $\mu_2 = 1/4$ (COMPAGNIE GÉNÉRALE DE GÉOPHYSIQUE, 1955, 1963, chart 83s) and the interpolation of the intermediate part is easily made.

Example 2. Construct graphically the following three-layer master curve (K-type):

$$\mu_2 = \rho_2/\rho_1 = 12; \quad \mu_3 = \rho_3/\rho_1 = 3$$
$$v_2 = h_2/h_1 = 4; \quad v_3 = h_3/h_1 = \infty$$

The procedure for construction of the field curve and the master curve is exactly the same, except that the point (1, 1) on the transparent graph sheet is put on the origin of the two-layer master curve, instead of the point (h_1, ρ_1), and the following steps are recommended:

(a) Consider this case initially as a two-layer problem with a resistivity ratio of $\mu_2 = 12^*$. Make the point (1, 1) on the graph

---

* Although the two-layer curve for $\mu_2 = 12$ is available (COMPAGNIE GÉNÉRALE DE GÉOPHYSIQUE, 1963), it is not included in the master curves presented in this book. This curve can, however, be easily constructed by interpolation, as explained on p.65.

sheet coincide with the origin of the master curves set, and draw
the curve corresponding to the given ratio $\mu_2 = 12$, as shown in
Fig.16B.

(*b*) Consider the top two layers as a single, reduced layer, and
find point K by means of K-point charts. For this, make the point
(1, 1) on the graph sheet coincide with the origin of K-point charts,

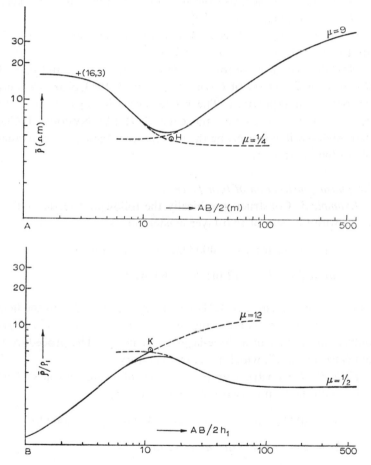

Fig.16A. Construction of a three-layer H-type field curve. $\rho_1 = 16\,\Omega m$, $\rho_2 = 4\,\Omega m$, $\rho_3 = 41\,\Omega m$, $h_1 = 3\,m$, $h_2 = 15\,m$, $h_3 = \infty$. B. Construction of three-layer K-type master curve. $\mu_2 = 12$, $\mu_3 = 3$, $\nu_2 = 4$, $\nu_3 = \infty$.

and K is located at the intersection of $\mu_2 = 12$ and $\nu_2 = 4$. This gives $\rho_K/\rho_1 = 6$ and $h_K/h_1 = 11.2$.

(c) With point K (6, 11.2) on the origin of the two-layer master curves (Plate II), draw the two-layer master curve for the resistivity ratio $\mu = \rho_3/\rho_K = (\rho_3/\rho_1)/(\rho_K/\rho_1) = 1/2$.

(d) For the intermediate part, a suitable three-layer master curve is not available; hence, use the principle of equivalence and keep T_2/T_1 constant, i.e., $\nu_2\mu_2 = \nu_2'\mu_2'$.

In this case, $\mu_2 = 12$, $\nu_2 = 4$, and the master curves available are for $\mu_2 = 9$; therefore, $\nu_2 = 5.3 \simeq 5$.

Now the master curve for $\nu_2 = 5$; $\mu_2 = 9$; $\nu_3 = \infty$, and $\mu_3 = 1$ (COMPAGNIE GÉNÉRALE DE GÉOPHYSIQUE, 1955, 1963, chart 60s) may be used for interpolation. The master curve for $\nu_2 = 5$; $\mu_2 = 9$; $\nu_3 = \infty$, and $\mu_3 = 3$—i.e., the curve EIR (ANONYMOUS, 1963a, plate 408)—will, however, be the first choice if these sets are available to the interpreter.

Graphical construction of four-layer curves

Example 3. Construct graphically the following four-layer field curve with the help of two-layer master curves:

$$\rho_1 = 100\ \Omega\text{m}; \quad \rho_2 = 400\ \Omega\text{m}; \quad \rho_3 = 20\ \Omega\text{m}; \quad \rho_4 = \infty$$

$$h_1 = 3\ \text{m}; \quad h_2 = 12\ \text{m}; \quad h_3 = 60\ \text{m}; \quad h_4 = \infty$$

This represents a curve of KH-type. It can be plotted with the help of two-layer master curves, and auxiliary point charts (K and H) only, as in the case of a three-layer construction. The procedure is indicated in Fig.17, which is self-explanatory.

Example 4. Construct graphically the following four-layer field curve with the help of two-layer master curves:

$$\rho_1 = 40\ \Omega\text{m}; \quad \rho_2 = 5\ \Omega\text{m}; \quad \rho_3 = 40\ \Omega\text{m}; \quad \rho_4 = 400\ \Omega\text{m}$$

$$h_1 = 2\ \text{m}; \quad h_2 = 3\ \text{m}; \quad h_3 = 12\ \text{m}; \quad h_4 = \infty$$

The plotting of a field curve represented by the above values has been shown in Fig.18, which is self-explanatory.

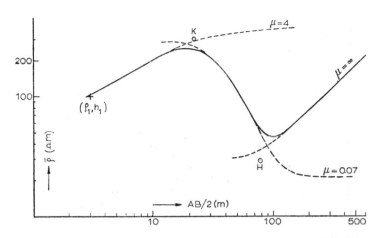

Fig.17. Construction of a four-layer KH-type field curve. $\rho_1 = 100\ \Omega m$. $\rho_2 = 400\ \Omega m$, $\rho_3 = 20\ \Omega m$, $\rho_4 = \infty$, $h_1 = 3$ m, $h_2 = 12$ m, $h_3 = 60$ m, $h_4 = \infty$.

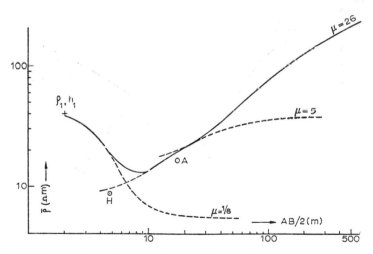

Fig.18. Construction of a four-layer HA-type field curve. $\rho_1 = 40\ \Omega m$, $\rho_2 = 5\ \Omega m$, $\rho_3 = 40\ \Omega m$, $\rho_4 = 400\ \Omega m$, $h_1 = 2$ m, $h_2 = 3$ m, $h_3 = 12$ m, $h_4 = \infty$.

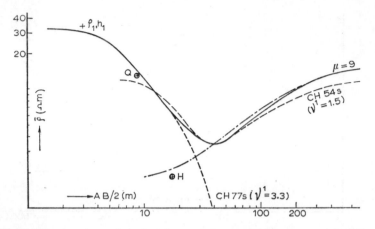

Fig.19. Construction of a four-layer QH-type field curve. $\rho_1 = 34\ \Omega m$, $\rho_2 = 12\ \Omega m$, $\rho_3 = 1\ \Omega m$, $\rho_4 = 16\ \Omega m$, $h_1 = 3\ m$, $h_2 = 7\ m$, $h_3 = 9\ m$, $h_4 = \infty$.

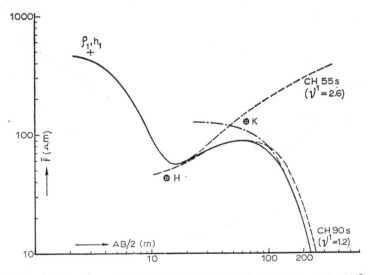

Fig.20. Construction of a four-layer HK-type field curve. $\rho_1 = 150\ \Omega m$, $\rho_2 = 10\ \Omega m$, $\rho_3 = 300\ \Omega m$, $\rho_4 = 0$, $h_1 = 3\ m$, $h_2 = 10\ m$, $h_3 = 20\ m$, $h_4 = \infty$.

Example 5. Construct graphically the following four-layer field curves with the help of three-layer and two-layer curves:

(a) $\rho_1 = 34\ \Omega m$; $\rho_2 = 12\ \Omega m$; $\rho_3 = 1\ \Omega m$; $\rho_4 = 16\ \Omega m$

$h_1 = 3\ m$; $h_2 = 7\ m$; $h_3 = 9\ m$; $h_4 = \infty$

(b) $\rho_1 = 150\ \Omega m$; $\rho_2 = 10\ \Omega m$; $\rho_3 = 300\ \Omega m$; $\rho_4 = 0$

$h_1 = 3\ m$; $h_2 = 10\ m$; $h_3 = 20\ m$; $h_4 = \infty$

The procedure is indicated in Fig.19 and 20, which are self-explanatory.

Qualitative interpretation of field curves

Example 6. Interpret qualitatively the given field curves (Fig.21), with the help of two-layer curves only (Plate II), to find ρ_1 and h_1. Take the value of ρ_2 equal to 11 Ωm, obtained from logging data.

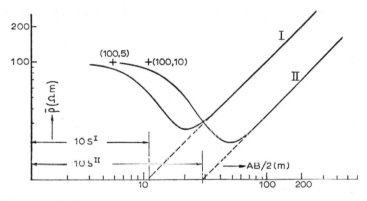

Fig.21. Qualitative interpretation of three-layer field curves. Interpretation by S-method, when lowermost layer is highly resistive; resistivity of second layer is known.

The following procedure may be adopted:

(a) The first part of the curve is matched with a two-layer curve (Plate II) to get ρ_1 and h_1. This gives, for curve *I*: $\rho_1 = 100\ \Omega m$, $h_1 = 5\ m$ and $S_1 = 0.05$; and for curve *II*: $\rho_1 = 100\ \Omega m$, $h_1 = 10\ m$ and $S_1 = 0.10$.

(b) The values of total S for the two curves are found, from the intersection of tangents to S-part at $\bar{\rho} = 1$, to be 1.0 and 2.9, respectively, for curves I and II.

(c) The values of h_2 given by $h_2 = \rho_2 \times S_2$, where $S_2 = S - S_1$, are 10.5 m and 30.8 m, respectively, for curve I and curve II.

Thus, the interpreted results for the curves are given as follows:

Curve I: $\rho_1 = 100\ \Omega\text{m}$; $h_1 = 5\ \text{m}$; $\rho_2 = 11\ \Omega\text{m}$; $h_2 = 10.5\ \text{m}$; $\rho_3 = \infty$.

Curve II: $\rho_1 = 100\ \Omega\text{m}$; $h_1 = 10\ \text{m}$; $\rho_2 = 11\ \Omega\text{m}$; $h_2 = 30.8\ \text{m}$; $\rho_3 = \infty$.

It may be mentioned here that the matching of these curves with the theoretical master curves gives $h_2 = 10$ m and 30 m, respectively, for curves I and II. Thus, the errors in the qualitative interpretation are, respectively, 5% and 2.5%.

Interpretation of three-layer field curves

   Example 7. Interpret the given K-type field curve (Fig.22) using

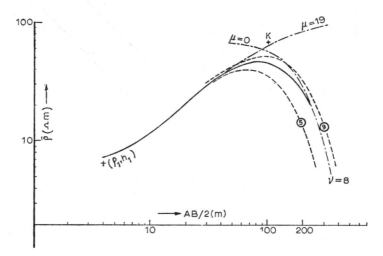

Fig.22. Quantitative interpretation of a three-layer K-type field curve. Two-, three-layer master curves; auxiliary point charts and Pylaev's nomograms used. Result: $\rho_1 = 7\ \Omega\text{m}$, $\rho_2 = 133\ \Omega\text{m}$, $\rho_3 = 0$, $h_1 = 5\ \text{m}$, $h_2 = 40\ \text{m}$, $h_3 = \infty$. Unbroken curve = field curve; dash-dot curve = two-layer master curve; dashed curve = three-layer master curve.

two- and three-layer theoretical master curves, auxiliary point charts and equivalent curves.

Interpretation of the three-layer field curve consists of the following steps:

(a) Try to match the left-hand part of the curve with a two-layer master curve, keeping in mind that the beginning of the given curve must asymptotically approach the abscissa $\bar{\rho}/\rho_1 = 1$.

A tolerably good match is obtained in the present case for $\mu_2 = \rho_2/\rho_1 = 19$ (Fig.22), with the left-hand cross-mark over the origin of the master curve.

The coordinates of the point are $\rho_1 = 7\,\Omega\text{m}$ and $h_1 = 5\,\text{m}$. Also, $\rho_2 = 19 \times 7 = 133\,\Omega\text{m}$.

(b) Try to match the entire three-layer curve with the point (7,5) on the origin of the standard three-layer master curves having $\mu_2 = 19$, $\rho_3 = 0$ for various values of ν_2 (refer to curves in COMPAGNIE GÉNÉRALE DE GÉOPHYSIQUE, 1955, 1963, chart 91s.). It is found that the field curve does not lie on any curve, but falls between $\nu = 5$ and 9. The value $\nu_2 = 8$ is obtained by interpolation (as shown in the diagram). This gives $h_2 = 8 \times h_1 = 40\,\text{m}$. The method of reading the value of ν_2 by interpolation and extrapolation has been explained in the note below.

(c) Now find the K-point with the help of auxiliary point charts (K-type), as indicated in the diagram, such that $\rho_K = 70\,\Omega\text{m}$ and $h_K = 100\,\text{m}$.

(d) With the K-point on the origin, try to find a match for the end part of the given curve with the two-layer set, and it is found that $\rho_3/\rho_K = 0$ gives a good match.

This provides a check on $\rho_3 = 0$, assumed while trying to match with the standard three-layer curves. The interpreted results finally obtained are noted on the diagram. In all these examples, the field curve, two-layer and three-layer master curves have been represented by solid line, dash-dot line and dashed lines, respectively.

Note: The curves presented in Fig.23 give the method of interpolation on a logarithm scale for two cases: (1) when the field curve lies between two master curves (Fig.23,a) and (2) when it lies outside the two master curves (Fig.23,*b*). The solid lines represent the field curves, and dashed lines the master curves.

The procedure is to cut out a piece of logarithm paper of the same modulus (62.5 mm) and superpose this on the divergent or parallel part of the curves. The same scale divisions as the difference in ν_2 values between the two master curves within or without which the field curve lies should be included if possible. A paper with a logarithm scale and a modulus of 62.5 mm may be used conveniently. If no such scale is available, one can be prepared by pasting cut-out portions of a graph sheet onto any paper scale. The beginning of a cycle must coincide with one of the master curves in question, as shown in the diagram. In Fig.23(*a*), the field curve lies between three-layer master curves for $\nu_2 = 2$ and 3. The interpolated value of ν_2 for the field curve is found to be equal to 2.4. In Fig.23(*b*) the field curve is outside $\nu_2 = 9$ and 24. The extrapolated value of ν_2 is found to be equal to 35.

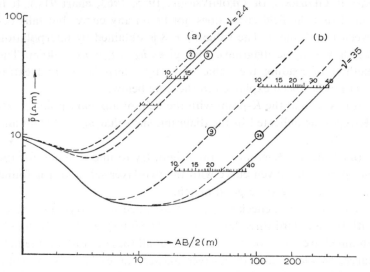

Fig.23. Method of reading by interpolation on logarithm scale. (*a*) Field curve lying between two master curves, interpolation. (*b*) Field curve lying outside two master curves, extrapolation. Beginning of a cycle coincided with the left hand master curve. Unbroken curve = field curve; dashed curve = three-layer master curve.

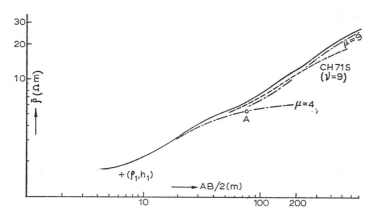

Fig.24. Quantitative interpretation of a three-layer A-type field curve. Results: $\rho_1 = 1.56\ \Omega\mathrm{m}$, $\rho_2 = 6.2\ \Omega\mathrm{m}$, $\rho_3 = 48.6\ \Omega\mathrm{m}$, $h_1 = 6\ \mathrm{m}$, $h_2 = 54\ \mathrm{m}$, $h_3 = \infty$. Unbroken curve = field curve; dash-dot curve = two-layer master curve; dashed curve = three-layer master curve.

Example 8. Interpret the given A-type three-layer field curve (Fig.24) with the help of the available two-layer and three-layer master curves. Use the charts available for determination of the auxiliary point (A-type, Plate III).

The procedure for interpretation is exactly the same as that in example 7, except that here the A-point is to be located instead of the H-point. The diagram (Fig.24) is self-explanatory and contains all the necessary details. The interpreted results are also noted on the diagram.

Example 9. Interpret the given Q-type field curve (Fig.25) with the help of available master curves and auxiliary point charts.

The actual procedure for interpretation has been indicated on the diagram itself, which is self-explanatory, and the results are also noted on the diagram.

Interpretation of four-layer and five-layer field curves

Example 10. Interpret the given four-layer KH-type field curve (Fig.26). Use three-layer and two-layer master curves and suitable auxiliary point charts for the purpose.

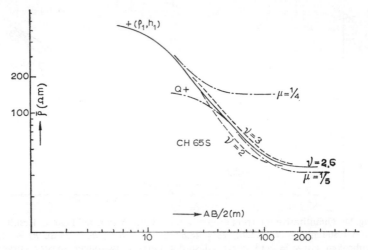

Fig.25. Quantitative interpretation of a three-layer Q-type field curve. Results: $\rho_1 = 560\ \Omega m$, $\rho_2 = 140\ \Omega m$, $\rho_3 = 35\ \Omega m$, $h_1 = 7$ m, $h_2 = 18.2$ m, $h_3 = \infty$. Unbroken curve = field curve; dash-dot curve = two-layer master curve; dashed curve = three-layer master curve.

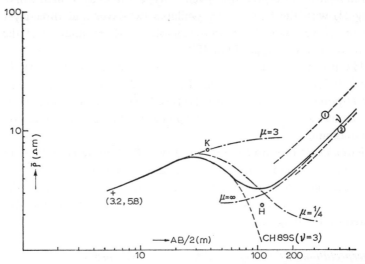

Fig.26. Quantitative interpretation of a four-layer KH-type field curve. Results: $\rho_1 = 3.2\ \Omega m$, $\rho_2 = 9.6\ \Omega m$, $\rho_3 = 1.75\ \Omega m$, $\rho_4 = \infty$, $h_1 = 5.8$ m, $h_2 = 23.2$ m, $h_3 = 68.4$ m, $h_4 = \infty$. Unbroken curve = field curve; dash-dot curve = two-layer master curve; dashed curve = three-layer master curve.

The following procedure may be adopted:

(a) On matching the left-hand part of the curve with a two-layer master curve (Plate I) the values of ρ_1 and h_1 are obtained, as indicated by the left-hand cross-mark. This gives $\rho_1 = 3.2\ \Omega m$, $h_1 = 5.8$ m and $\mu_2 = 3$.

(b) The values obtained in step (a) are used in choosing the right set of three-layer master curves. The first part (K-type) is then superposed over the curve chart 89s in the COMPAGNIE GÉNÉRALE DE GÉOPHYSIQUE (1955, 1963), and, on matching, the value of ν_2 is found to be equal to 3. This set relates to $\mu_2 = 4$ and not $\mu_2 = 3$; therefore, the value of ν_2 must be corrected (ν_2') by the principle of equivalence with the help of the relation: $\nu_2\mu_2 = \nu_2'\mu_2'$ giving $\nu_2' = 4$. Then, $\rho_2 = 9.6\ \Omega m$ and $h_2 = 4 \times 5.8 = 23.2$ m.

(c) Note the K-point with the help of K-type auxiliary point charts (Plate IV) at the intersection of $\mu_2 = 3$ and $\nu_2 = 4$, with the (ρ_1, h_1) point on the origin.

(d) Match with the two-layer master curves (Plate II), keeping K on the origin to get the value of $\mu = \rho_3/\rho_K$ in order to decide on the next three-layer curve for matching. This gives $\mu = 1/4$.

(e) Superpose (with the K-point on the origin) the last three-layer curve (H-type) on COMPAGNIE GÉNÉRALE DE GÉOPHYSIQUE (1955, 1963) chart 83s ($\rho_2/\rho_1 = 1/4$ and $\rho_3 = \infty$), and the following values are obtained by matching: $\mu = \rho_3/\rho_K = 1/4$, $\nu = h_3/h_K = 1.8$ (read by interpolation) and $\rho_4/\rho_K = \infty$, i.e., $\rho_4 = \infty$.

(f) In order to check the value of ρ_4, the H-point is now found out with the help of Plate III from the values of μ and ν obtained in step (e), keeping the origin at the K-point. A match with two-layer curves (Plate I) with reference to the H-point gives $\rho_4/\rho_H = \infty$, and hence the value of ρ_4 is checked.

The interpreted values are noted on the diagram (Fig.26).

Example 11. Interpret the given five-layer (KHK-type) field curve (Fig.27).

The procedure is indicated on the diagram, which is self-explanatory, with final results noted over this.

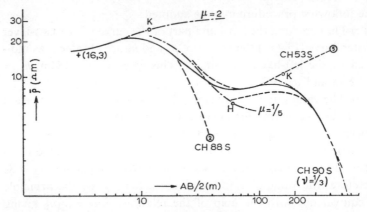

Fig.27. Quantitative interpretation of a multi-layer field curve. Five layers identified. Results: $\rho_1 = 16\ \Omega\text{m}$, $\rho_2 = 32\ \Omega\text{m}$, $\rho_3 = 5\ \Omega\text{m}$, $\rho_4 = 54\ \Omega\text{m}$, $\rho_5 = 0$, $h_1 = 3$ m, $h_2 = 6.9$ m, $h_3 = 48$ m, $h_4 = 20$ m, $h_5 = \infty$. Unbroken curve = = field curve; dash-dot curve = two-layer master curve; dashed curve = three-layer master curve.

PROBLEMS

Problem on interpolation

Problem 1. Construct graphically the following two-layer master curves by exact graphical interpolation for the following cases (with the help of available two-layer master curves). Explain the procedure.

    (*a*) $\mu_2 = 11$ and $\mu_2 = 1/11$
    (*b*) $\mu_2 = 15$ and $\mu_2 = 1/15$
    (*c*) $\mu_2 = 25$ and $\mu_2 = 1/25$
    (*d*) $\mu_2 = 35$ and $\mu_2 = 1/35$
    (*e*) $\mu_2 = 44$ and $\mu_2 = 1/44$
    (*f*) $\mu_2 = 31$ and $\mu_2 = 1/31$
    (*g*) $\mu_2 = \ \ 5$ and $\mu_2 = 1/5$
    (*h*) $\mu_2 = 50$ and $\mu_2 = 1/50$

Problem on three-layer graphical construction

Problem 2. Construct graphically the three-layer vertical electrical sounding (V.E.S.) curves with the values given in Table IV.

TABLE IV

VALUES OF THE PARAMETERS
FOR THREE-LAYER SCHLUMBERGER V.E.S. CURVES

V.E.S.	$\rho_1\ (\Omega m)$	$h_1\ (m)$	$\rho_2\ (\Omega m)$	$h_2\ (m)$	$\rho_3\ (\Omega m)$
1	20	10	80	20	20
2	6	4	30	12	4
3	100	2	600	6	80
4	4	16	100	50	10
5	1	4	3	6	0
6	1	4	6	3	100
7	5	25	20	10	∞
8	10	100	120	80	∞
9	15	10	100	15	600
10	100	2	2	10	150
11	70	3	50	15	100
12	150	10	6	20	∞
13	10	5	5	5	3
14	75	10	25	20	0

Use the master curves, auxiliary point charts and Pylaev's nomograms whenever necessary.

Problem on four-layer graphical construction

Problem 3. Construct graphically the four-layer vertical electrical sounding curves for the values given in Table V. Use theoretical master curves, auxiliary point charts and Pylaev's nomograms.

Problem on qualitative interpretation

Problem 4. Plot the field curve on transparent double-logarithm graph sheet with a modulus of 62.5 mm from the values of the apparent resistivity and corresponding half-electrode separation given in Table VI. Interpret the curves qualitatively with the given values of the resistivity of the second layer. Only two-layer master curves may be used.

$\rho_2 = 180\ \Omega m$ for V.E.S.-1, $160\ \Omega m$ for V.E.S.-2, $6\ \Omega m$ for V.E.S.-3, $11\ \Omega m$ for V.E.S.-4, $9\ \Omega m$ for V.E.S.-5 and $48\ \Omega m$ for V.E.S.-6.

TABLE V

VALUES OF THE PARAMETERS
FOR FOUR-LAYER SCHLUMBERGER V.E.S. CURVES

V.E.S. No.	Type curve	ρ_1 (Ωm)	h_1 (m)	ρ_2 (Ωm)	h_2 (m)	ρ_3 (Ωm)	h_3 (m)	ρ_4 (Ωm)
1	AA	15	5	150	15	600	50	∞
2	AA	10	10	50	30	300	80	∞
3	AA	15	5	10	10	80	40	500
4	AK	10	1	40	10	160	25	0
5	AK	10	5	30	10	60	20	10
6	AK	50	4	100	16	300	48	0
7	KQ	5	3	15	10	5	20	0
8	KQ	10	1	100	2	10	4	0
9	KQ	10	2	100	4	20	8	10
10	QQ	100	5	50	10	25	20	0
11	QQ	50	1	10	5	1	15	0
12	QQ	500	1	250	5	100	10	50
13	KH	10	1	40	3	30	20	∞
14	KH	15	10	300	20	3	40	10
15	KH	5	10	70	10	10	20	∞
16	KH	3	5	20	10	10	25	100
17	QH	100	2	10	10	1	20	10
18	QH	200	2	40	4	15	10	200
19	QH	50	5	250	50	10	100	25
20	HA	100	5	20	10	150	50	∞
21	HA	10	2	1	4	10	10	100
22	HA	500	1	50	10	500	50	∞
23	HK	150	3	10	10	300	20	0
24	HK	200	5	50	10	500	30	50
25	HK	100	15	10	50	150	200	20

Problems on quantitative interpretation

Problem. 5 Plot the three-layer field curves on double-logarithm graph sheet with a modulus of 62.5 mm from the values given in Tables VII and VIII; then interpret the curves with the help of available two- and three-layer master curves, and the auxiliary point charts. The principle of equivalence should be used wherever necessary.

Problem 6. Plot the four-layer field curves from the values given in Table IX, and then interpret the curves with the help of three-layer master curves as far as practicable. Two-layer master curves

TABLE VI

APPARENT RESISTIVITY AND CORRESPONDING HALF-ELECTRODE SEPARATION

(DATA FOR THREE-LAYER SCHLUMBERGER FIELD CURVES)

Resistivity (Ωm)

AB/2 (m):	2	3	4	5	6	8	10	15	20	30	40	50	80	100	150	200	300	400	600	800
V.E.S.																				
1	120	125	129	132	135	144	151	180	210	285	368	458	720	890	1,275	1,680	2,550	3,400	5,000	6,400
2	64	68	72	77	83	92	100	122	135	163	190	222	340	438	640	840	1,300	1,740	2,650	3,500
3	220	220	216	210	201	183	166	120	85	73	88	109	172	220	322	436	660	870	1,300	1,735
4	98	98	93	85	78	62	48	30	29	38	50	64	103	130	190	260	390	515	800	1,050
5	180	178	164	150	128	92	64	30	23	24	32	40	64	80	120	160	242	320	480	640
6	130	130	130	130	131	132	134	145	160	190	221	250	308	320	380	420	500	560	790	990

TABLE VII

APPARENT RESISTIVITY AND CORRESPONDING HALF-ELECTRODE SEPARATION
(DATA FOR THREE-LAYER SCHLUMBERGER H- AND K-TYPE FIELD CURVES)

Resistivity (Ωm)

AB/2 (m):	2	3	4	5	6	8	10	15	20	30	40	50	80	100	150	200	300	400	600	800
V.E.S.																				
1	380	380	366	345	320	270	224	128	70	48	60	72	108	124	160	190	240	275	—	—
2	—	620	620	610	600	540	460	300	190	85	60	58	71	77	86	90	96	100	100	100
3	6.9	7.0	7.4	8.3	9.1	11	12.5	17	22	32	38	43	47	45	36	25	13	—	—	—
4	50	50	49	48	47	45	40	28	20	9.4	4.9	2.8	2.8	3.6	5.9	8.7	15	21	36	—
5	20	20	21	22	23	27	30	36	36	28	19	12	5.2	3.8	1.3	1.2	1.2	1.2	1.2	1.2
6	—	—	—	—	33	33	33	33	32	41	50	60	80	88	92	83	54	30	16	—
7	34	34	33	31	28	22	18	10	6.9	6.1	7.4	9.2	13.5	14.5	22	27.5	37	47	65	80
8	4.8	6.1	7.4	8.6	9.9	12	13.2	15	14.8	12.2	9.2	7.3	4.7	4.3	4.1	3.9	—	—	—	—

TABLE VIII

APPARENT RESISTIVITY AND CORRESPONDING HALF-ELECTRODE SEPARATION
(DATA FOR THREE-LAYER SCHLUMBERGER A- AND Q-TYPE FIELD CURVES)

Resistivity (Ωm)

AB/2 (m):	2	3	4	5	6	8	10	15	20	30	40	50	80	100	150	200	300	400	600	800
V.E.S.																				
1	50	56	62	67	72	79	85	100	110	130	146	160	181	192	210	220	225	226	227	228
2	19	22	25.5	29	33	33	43	54	62	78	93	108	144	158	185	205	240	245	248	250
3	17	18	20	22	24	23	31	38	45	54	60	68	86	95	125	150	182	210	240	250
4	13	14.5	16	18	20	24	27	33	37	44	52	59	81	93	114	130	146	156	170	—
5	—	8.1	8.1	8.5	9.3	10.2	11.2	14.1	17	21.5	25	27.5	34	40	55	74	120	—	—	—
6	38	39	40	42	44	43	53	61	68	76	85	93	118	133	190	250	365	495	760	—
7	50	49	48	47	47	45	43	36	29	20	16	13	9.4	7.9	5.6	4.4	3.6	3.5	3.4	3.3
8	44	43	42	42	41	38	34	23	15	7.1	3.6	2.1	0.82	0.70	0.60	0.58	—	—	—	—
9	—	—	—	—	76	76	75	74	70	66	62	59	52	48	41	33	16	7.2	2.6	1.1
10	—	—	—	—	100	100	100	99	98	90	80	65	26	25	14.5	12	9.8	8.2	3.8	1.7

TABLE IX

APPARENT RESISTIVITY AND CORRESPONDING HALF-ELECTRODE
SEPARATION (DATA FOR FOUR-LAYER SCHLUMBERGER FIELD CURVES)

AB/2 (m):	Resistivity (Ωm)																			
	2	3	4	5	6	8	10	15	20	30	40	60	80	100	150	200	300	400	600	800
V.E.S.																				
1	186	186	187	203	220	250	280	360	430	490	485	350	265	196	94	42	—	—	—	—
2	52	62	74	86	100	126	155	211	240	265	265	210	150	105	50	32	36	46	78	88
3	—	28	28	29	30	32.5	36.3	45	53.5	69	74	115	140	160	195	340	215	150	—	—
4	56	56	50	44	40	33	28	21	17.5	14.4	13.3	13.4	14.3	17	26	36	60	—	—	—
5	—	51	51	52	50	45	42	33	26	16.6	12.0	11.4	11.4	10.5	7.6	5.1	2.2	—	—	—
6	—	4.4	4.4	4.6	4.8	5.2	5.8	6.9	7.7	8.4	7.8	5.8	4.8	4.7	5.4	6.8	9.8	12.6	18	20
7	17	13.5	10.0	7.5	6.0	4.0	3.2	3.2	3.8	4.9	5.8	6.8	7.0	6.6	5.0	3.4	1.8	1.5	1.3	1.3
8	—	30	30	30	29.5	28	25	18	13	7.8	5.6	4.0	3.4	2.9	2.1	1.5	0.7	—	—	—
9	122	97	96	52	39	19	9.2	8.1	10	15	20	30	40	50	75	100	150	205	310	410
10	42	38	37.5	34	30	20.5	15.5	8.4	6.1	4.9	5.1	7.1	8.6	10.0	13.4	15.6	18.6	19.4	20	20
11	31	27.7	26.7	26	23	15.4	11	5.6	3.7	2.4	4.1	5.2	6.2	7.0	8.5	9.8	11.5	12.5	13	13
12	1.10	1.14	1.20	1.25	1.32	1.46	1.60	1.87	2.14	2.6	3.0	3.7	4.4	5.0	6.3	7.4	9.3	10.7	11.8	—

TABLE X

APPARENT RESISTIVITY AND HALF-ELECTRODE SEPARATION
(DATA FOR MULTI-LAYER SCHLUMBERGER FIELD CURVES)

AB/2 (m):	2	3	4	5	6	8	10	15	20	30	40	50	80	100	150	200	300	400	600	800
V.E.S.								Resistivity (Ωm)												
HAKQH	50	33	25	23	24	31	38	55	71	98	122	138	150	145	118	88	47	33	32	42
AKQK	200	258	340	400	450	500	500	400	285	154	124	94	83	82	81	72	46	24	–	–
HKQK	14	8.2	6.9	7.4	8.2	9.5	10.5	11.0	10.4	8.8	7.7	7.2	6.5	6.3	6.2	5.8	4.4	2.7	–	–
AKH	21	28	36	45	35	71	84	91	71	47	36	29	33	41	54	66	84	91	94	94

may be used for checking, and if unavoidable. Auxiliary point charts may be used. The principle of equivalence must be used wherever necessary, showing exact limits of equivalence for the specific cases. Use logarithm graph sheet with a modulus of 62.5 mm.

Problem 7. Interpret the multi-layer field curves plotted from the values given in Table X, with the help of three-layer master curves, auxiliary point charts and, wherever necessary, the principle of equivalence. Use graph sheet with a modulus equal to 62.5 mm.

CHAPTER 4

Wenner Sounding

In this section we shall discuss briefly the methods and techniques available for interpretation of Wenner sounding curves. It appears that in English-speaking countries the Wenner configuration is used almost exclusively, whereas in many European and Asian countries (including France, the U.S.S.R., and China) the Schlumberger configuration is preferred. It will be worthwhile at this stage to compare the characteristic performances of the Schlumberger and Wenner methods.

COMPARISON OF SCHLUMBERGER AND WENNER METHODS

The Schlumberger theoretical master curves are based on the value of electric field intensity at the sounding stations, whereas the Wenner curves utilize the potential difference between M and N. Hence the Schlumberger and Wenner methods are sometimes known as *gradient* and *potential* methods, respectively. It has been shown in Chapter 3, and will be further demonstrated here, that measurement with either of these arrangements tends toward the same asymptotic values.

As the names suggest, the anomaly in the Schlumberger or gradient method is rounded off, and the minor distortions are not indicated. Wenner curves, in contrast, retain these distortions and undulations, which are due to local inhomogeneities; as these are normally irregularly scattered in the ground, they are not important from a practical point of view.

While the electrical properties of the various layers are reflected to a remarkable degree in the Schlumberger curve, the theoretical condition that $(MN/AB) \to 0$, required for apparent resistivity calculation, is never fulfilled in practice. In Wenner's method, such difficulties are not met with, since (MN/AB) is constant (1/3).

In the gradient method, MN is changed after a number of changes in AB; this cuts the working hours by about 50%. The cable length is reduced, and cable continuity as well as leakage locations in potential cables can be easily checked and detected.

The introduction of personal error in the Schlumberger method is small, since only two electrodes are changed at a time (rather than all four).

The Wenner method is sensitive to near-surface inhomogeneities, but cannot always clearly resolve deeper events (DEPPERMANN, 1954). The master curves (MOONEY and WETZEL, 1956) available for the potential method have been plotted for shallower events only. In the case of four-layer curves, asymptotic parts have not been plotted for a large number of cases.

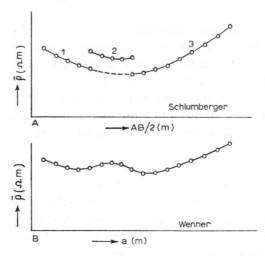

Fig.28. Characteristic curves for Wenner and Schlumberger arrangements. Segments *1*, *2* and *3* in Schlumberger arrangement correspond to the three locations of potential electrodes.

The Schlumberger configuration can account for both near-surface inhomogeneities and deeper events. In Fig.28, the segment numbered 2 (for a given value of MN) has been raised against the normal trend, indicating the presence of a local inhomogeneity; the actual trend for deeper events is obtained by interpolation (Fig.28), as shown by the dotted curve for a laterally homogeneous earth (DE GERY and KUNETZ, 1956). Since a local inhomogeneity existed near one or both of the potential electrodes when MN has the second value used, segment 2 of the curve is displaced upward with respect to the other two segments. Segments 1 and 3 can be connected easily by moving segment 2 downward to its correct position (shown by the dotted line). The lower curve illustrates, for example, what might have been obtained with the Wenner configuration as it is normally used. On the smooth Wenner curve, the effect of the local inhomogeneity cannot be differentiated from the effects from deep horizontal discontinuities.

The most important advantage of the Schlumberger arrangement is that the analytic-graphical method of construction of empirical curves (explained in Chapter 3) is applicable only in the case of "gradient arrangement". Also, the technique of partial matching, applicable to the interpretation of multi-layer curves, is possible with sufficient accuracy only in the case of the Schlumberger arrangement. On the other hand, the similar grapho-analytical approach and the technique of partial matching are not available in the Wenner "potential method".

In the interpretation of multi-layer Wenner field curves through the use of two- and three-layer theoretical master curves, i.e., by partial matching, Hummel proposed the reduction of two surface layers to a single equivalent layer; he noted that this approximation applies only for electrode spacing that is large compared with the thicknesses of the two surface layers. Also, to apply the partial match successfully, the second layer should be appreciably thicker than the surface layer (MOONEY, 1954). The most important condition for the applicability of Hummel's rule with sufficient accuracy is that the three-layer curve must have a minimum. This means that this rule is valid, strictly speaking, only for the H-type curve.

ASYMPTOTIC VALUES AND AVAILABLE THEORETICAL CURVES

The apparent resistivity relation for a two-layer earth may be written for the Wenner arrangement —see eq.(2.54)—as:

$$\bar{\rho} = \rho_1 \left[1 + 4 \sum_{n=1}^{\infty} \left\{ \frac{K_{12}^n}{[1 + (2nh_1/a)^2]^{\frac{1}{2}}} - \frac{K_{12}^n}{[4 + (2nh_1/a)^2]^{\frac{1}{2}}} \right\} \right] \quad (4.1)$$

As in the case of the Schlumberger arrangement—eq.(3.1)—the above eq.(4.1) also gives the following limiting cases:

(*1*) When $\rho_2 = \rho_1$, $\bar{\rho} = \rho_1$

(*2*) When $a \to 0$, $\bar{\rho} = \rho_1$

(*3*) When $a \to \infty$, $\bar{\rho} = \rho_2$

Since ρ_1 and ρ_2 are known from the first and the last parts of the field curve, respectively, the depth to the second layer (h_1) can easily be found. Tagg's method of interpretation may be used (TAGG, 1964). Nowadays this method is not widely used since a large number of curves are available for curve matching. Also, Tagg's method cannot be used unless one is quite sure of two layers. This method, however, is briefly explained in the next section for comparison purposes only. The curve-matching technique is discussed on p.106.

We can show, as in the case of Schlumberger (Chapter 3), that for a multi-layer earth the asymptotic nature is still retained on a double-logarithm scale. Thus, a total matching of field curves with the theoretically plotted master curves may be done for the interpretation of field data.

Theoretical three-layer and four-layer master curves for Wenner sounding are available in published form (MOONEY and WETZEL, 1956). The total number of Wenner curves is 2,300. Only 15% of these are three-layer ones, the remainder representing four-layer cases. A set of two-layer curves is also included to complete the set. All these curves are plotted on double-logarithm graph sheets with a modulus equal to 5 inches. The available three-layer master curves may be classified into four types (as in the case of Schlumberger) with the values of the parameters as given in Table XI.

TABLE XI

PARAMETERS FOR THREE-LAYER WENNER MASTER CURVES

Curve type	ρ_2/ρ_1	Corresponding ρ_3/ρ_1
H	1/3	100, 10, 3, 1
	1/10	100, 10, 3, 1, 1/3
	1/100	10, 3, 1, 1/3, 1/10
A	10	100
	3	100, 10
	100	10, 3, 1, 1/3, 1/10, 1/100
K	10	3, 1, 1/3, 1/10, 1/100
	3	1, 1/3, 1/10, 1/100
Q	1/3	1/10, 1/100
	1/10	1/100

All of the above curves have been plotted for ten different values of $v_2 = h_2/h_1 = 1/4, 1/3, 1/2, 2/3, 1, 3/2, 2, 3, 4$ and 5, making a total of 350 three-layer curves available for interpretation.

In the case of the four-layer curves, the last asymptotic part of a number of the sets have not been drawn. For this reason the interpreter sometimes faces serious difficulties in matching the field curves. In a recent set of tables and charts for Wenner arrangement (ORELLANA and MOONEY, 1966) more accuracy has been claimed.

TAGG'S METHOD OF INTERPRETATION

Two-layer case

A direct method of depth interpretation is achieved in this case by Tagg's method. This method establishes a number of simultaneous equations, giving depth h as a function of the resistivity factor K.

Eq.(4.1) indicates that the apparent resistivity for a given electrode separation (i.e., $a = $ constant) is only a function of h and K. Thus, theoretically, two resistivity values for two electrode separations are sufficient to obtain both h and K. In practice, several equations are set up for various electrode separations, and depths are obtained graphically.

For graphical interpretation the following procedure may be adopted (TAGG, 1964):

(*1*) Read the value of ρ_1, the resistivity of the surface layer, by extrapolation of the field curve plotted with the separation (*a*) along the abscissa and $\bar{\rho}$ along the ordinate. When the value of ρ_1 cannot be found by extrapolation, the resistivities for the first few values of small electrode separation are averaged out; the mean resistivity is then taken as ρ_1.

(*2*) Note the value of apparent resistivity $\bar{\rho}^{(1)}$ corresponding to a certain value of electrode separation a_1, and calculate $\bar{\rho}^{(1)}/\rho_1$.

(*3*) Tabulate the values of (*h/a*), one for each value of *K*, corresponding to the particular value of $\bar{\rho}^{(1)}/\rho_1$. These are obtained from the set of master curves (TAGG, 1964) ($\bar{\rho}/\rho_1$ vs. *h/a*), plotted for various values of *K*. These curves are plotted on a linear scale and can be found in several textbooks in the English language (see, for example, DOBRIN, 1960; TAGG, 1964).

(*4*) Multiply the values of *h/a* obtained in step (*3*) by the corresponding value of electrode separation to give the values of *h*, one for each value of *K*.

(*5*) Plot the tabulated values of *h* and *K* and draw a smooth curve.

(*6*) Choose a second value of $a = a_2$ and repeat the above procedure to get a second curve of *h* against *K*.

(*7*) Read the value of *h* and *K* corresponding to the intersection of the above two curves. ρ_2 is calculated from the value of *K* so obtained.

(*8*) Repeat the whole process with an additional value of "*a*" and obtain a third curve to ensure the accuracy of interpretation. If the three curves do not intersect at a point, the center of the triangle so formed may be taken to give the value of *h* and *K*.

Three-layer case

Tagg's method can be extended to the three-layer case by the method of successive approximation, provided the third layer does not appreciably influence the first part of the curve. This is valid when the thickness of the second layer is two to three times the thickness of the top layer. Use is made of the empirical relation between the point of inflection on the right-hand part of the curve and the depth of the lower layer ($h_1 + h_2$). In the case of a highly resistive third layer, it is seen that this depth may be taken as 2/3 times the electrode separation at which the point of inflection occurs.

The following steps may be adopted:

(*1*) Determine the value of ρ_1 as accurately as possible by taking small electrode intervals and averaging these values.

(*2*) Now, considering the first part of the curve as a two-layer case, proceed as outlined in the two-layer case above, and note the value of h_1 and ρ_2.

(*3*) Calculate $H = h_1 + h_2$—i.e., the depth to the third layer—by using the empirical relation $h_1 + h_2 = (2/3)d$ already mentioned.

(*4*) Determine the effective resistivity ρ_e of the reduced layer, combining the first two, given by the formula due to Hummel:

$$(h_1 + h_2)/\rho_e = h_1/\rho_1 + h_2/\rho_2$$

(*5*) Treat the section as a two-layer case having resistivities ρ_e and ρ_3, and the total thickness $h_1 + h_2$. Apply the two-layer method now to the last part of the curve to get the value of ρ_3. Repeat the previous step with successive values of ($h_1 + h_2$) to get a more refined and accurate value.

As mentioned earlier, the procedure for interpretation of three-layer curves by Tagg's method holds good for H-type only. After the appearance of a large number of two-, three- and four-layer master curves plotted on double-logarithm papers, most of the significance of Tagg's method is lost. Thus, when these master curves are available, Tagg's method of interpretation is seldom used. However, despite its serious limitations, Tagg's method sometimes provides a useful method of interpretation in a simple two-layer case.

INTERPRETATION BY CURVE MATCHING

We have already enlisted the various two-, three- and four-layer theoretical master curves available for interpretation of Wenner curves. Now we shall explain, in brief, how these curves by MOONEY and WETZEL (1956) are used for interpretation by curve-matching. Mooney and Wetzel, in presenting the master curves for Wenner configuration, have used the notations R, D and a, representing, respectively, resistivity (ρ), depth (h) and separation $(AB/2)$.

The following steps are recommended:

(*1*) Plot the field data on a transparent double-logarithm graph sheet with a modulus equal to 5 inches (the same as for the theoretical curves) with $\bar{\rho}$ as ordinate and separation "a" as abscissa.

(*2*) Superpose the field curve on the various sets of theoretical curves until a good match is found. Keep the axes parallel.

(*3*) Read out the apparent resistivity value on the field curve which overlies $R_a = 1$ on the theoretical curve. This gives R_1.

(*4*) Note the electrode separation on the field curve which overlies $a = 6$ on the theoretical master curve. This gives D_2 for a three-layer case and D_3 for a four-layer one.

(*5*) Note the depth ratio which identifies the theoretical curve, i.e., $D_1 : D_2 : D_3$ for a three-layer one.

(*6*) Then read the resistivity ratio for the group of curves with which the field curve is matched. This gives $R_1 : R_2 : R_3$ and $R_1 : R_2 : R_3 : R_4$ for the three- and four-layer cases, respectively.

Thus, from the values read out in the above steps, the values of the resistivities ρ_1, ρ_2, ρ_3 etc., and thicknesses h_1, h_2 etc., are easily calculated. This is explained in the example immediately following.

It should be remembered that in many cases the field curves cannot be matched fully with the available theoretical curves. In such cases some interpolation between curves will be necessary.

EXAMPLE

Fig.29 shows the matched condition of a four-layer field curve

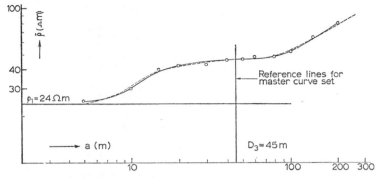

Fig.29. Quantitative interpretation of a four-layer Wenner field curve. Complete matching with the set of master curves by MOONEY and WETZEL (1956). Results: $\rho_1 = 24\ \Omega$m, $\rho_2 = 72\ \Omega$m, $\rho_3 = 8\ \Omega$m, $\rho_4 = 240\ \Omega$m. $h_1 = 7.5$ m, $h_2 = 22.5$ m, $h_3 = 15$ m, $h_4 = \infty$. $R_1:R_2:R_3:R_4 = 1:3:1/3:10$. $D_1:D_2:D_3 = 1:4:6$. Unbroken curve = field curve; dashed curve = four-layer master curve.

(KELLY, 1962) on a suitable theoretical four-layer curve wherefrom the following values are obtained:

  (a) $R_1 = 24\ \Omega$m

  (b) $D_3 = 45$ m

  (c) $D_1:D_2:D_3 = 1:4:6$

  (d) $R_1:R_2:R_3:R_4 = 1:3:1/3:10$

The resistivities (ρ_1, ρ_2, ρ_3 and ρ_4) and thicknesses (h_1, h_2 and h_3) of the individual layers are indicated within the diagram.

PROBLEMS

Problem 1

Plot the three-layer (V.E.S.) curves for Wenner arrangement (on a transparent double-logarithm graph sheet of 5-inch modulus) from the values given in Table XII. Interpret the curves with the help of the album of master curves by MOONEY and WETZEL (1956) by means of the well-known complete curve-matching technique.

TABLE XII

APPARENT RESISTIVITY AND CORRESPONDING ELECTRODE SEPARATION
(DATA FOR THREE-LAYER WENNER FIELD CURVES)

a (m):	4.5	6	7.5	9	10.5	12	15	18	24	30	45	60	75	90	120	150	225	300	450
V.E.S.																			
1	15.9	16	16	17	23	18.7	21	22	24.5	31	40	46.5	51	53	54	54	53	52	—
2	—	15.8	16	16	16.5	17.4	18.3	19.3	21.4	23.5	28	30.4	32.5	33	32.6	31	27.5	—	—
3	21.2	21.4	21.5	22.4	23	23.8	24.7	25.5	26.8	27.5	28.5	28	27	26	24	22.2	19	14.4	8.3
4	13.1	13.1	13.2	13.4	13.5	14.6	15	16	17.9	19.4	21	21	20	18.4	14.8	11.8	7.6	—	—
5	—	—	—	4.7	4.7	4.7	4.8	4.9	5.5	6.1	8.0	9.8	11.4	13	16.2	19	24	29	—
6	—	—	—	4.6	4.6	4.6	4.6	4.7	4.9	5.2	6.3	7.5	8.8	10	12	13.3	14.5	14.4	—
7	—	—	11.2	11.2	11	10.7	10	9.4	7.9	6.2	3.8	3.1	3.2	3.7	4.6	5.6	8.2	10.8	—

Resistivity (Ωm)

TABLE XIII

APPARENT RESISTIVITY AND CORRESPONDING ELECTRODE SEPARATION
(DATA FOR FOUR-LAYER WENNER FIELD CURVES)

a (m):	4.5	6	7.5	9	10.5	12	15	18	24	30	45	60	75	90	120	150	225	300	450
V.E.S.																			
1	–	–	–	14.1	14.1	14.2	14.3	14.8	16	17.3	21	24	26.4	27.6	27	25	18	11.3	4.2
2	8.2	8.3	8.6	9.0	9.4	10	11	12	14	15.5	17.2	17.2	16	15.6	13.4	11.9	9.8	8.8	–
3	6.8	7.2	7.7	8.3	9.0	9.5	10.8	11.5	12.7	13.1	12.4	10.3	8.0	6.3	4.3	3.35	3.05	3.30	4.1
4	–	–	4.1	4.1	4.1	4.2	4.4	4.65	5.2	5.75	7.4	9.4	11.3	13	16.2	19.3	26.6	33.3	46
5	5.9	5.8	5.4	5.1	4.7	4.36	3.9	3.6	3.4	3.5	4.4	5.6	7.0	8.3	11	13.8	20	26.5	–
6	5.9	5.55	5.4	4.8	4.4	4.1	3.55	3.2	2.9	2.9	3.4	4.2	5.0	5.8	7.2	8.2	10.2	10.8	10.4

Resistivity (Ωm)

Problem 2

Plot the four-layer (V.E.S.) curves for Wenner arrangement from the values given in Table XIII, and then interpret the curves by complete curve-matching. Use double-logarithm graph sheets of 5-inch modulus.

CHAPTER 5

Dipole Sounding

The various dipole arrangements have been explained and the apparent resistivity relations derived in Chapter 2. It has been proved there (in the section on D.E.S.) that the apparent resistivity, as measured by any of the dipole arrangements, is related to that obtained by conventional Schlumberger arrangement —as given by eq.(2.81)–(2.84). This brings in the possibility of construction of dipole electric sounding curves from conventional Schlumberger curves. It is interesting to note that the azimuthal resistivity $\bar{\rho}_\theta$ is equal to the Schlumberger apparent resistivity $\bar{\rho}$ for the same spacing, $\bar{R} = AO = AB/2$ (see Fig.30). This means that the master curves available for conventional sounding may be used directly for azimuthal dipole sounding, the method of interpretation remaining the same.

In this chapter we have outlined in brief some characteristic features of dipole electric sounding, and have followed this with a possible field layout for equatorial arrangement. A list of available curves has been included, and the method of interpretation ex-

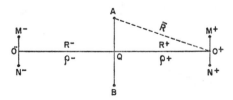

Fig.30. Bilateral equatorial arrangement. $QO = R$, separation; $AO = \bar{R}$, effective distance in equatorial dipole arrangement. "Plus" when MN is towards contact (inclined bed), "minus" when MN is away from the contact.

plained. Some problems on radial dipole sounding have been added. Since for equatorial arrangement the theoretical master curves and the method of interpretation remain the same as for conventional sounding (Chapter 3), we have avoided repetition by not including any further examples or problems.

CHARACTERISTICS OF DIPOLE SOUNDING

Dipole electric sounding differs from conventional sounding in its inherent possibility for bilateral and multilateral measurements. This is explained in Fig.30 for the equatorial arrangement. For a certain position of the current dipole AB, two potential dipoles M^+N^+ and M^-N^- can be placed on either side at distances R^+ and R^-. Thus, for a certain arrangement two values of resistivity ρ^+ and ρ^- are obtained, corresponding to the mid-points of QO^+ and QO^-, respectively. The arrangement, usually meant for dipping layers, may be called a two-way sounding, or bilateral sounding. The symbols "+" and "−" indicate, respectively, whether the moving electrodes in an arrangement are moving towards the contact or away from it.

For a horizontally stratified earth, the values of both resistivity ρ^+ and ρ^- will be the same. For an inclined horizon, the values of ρ^+ and ρ^- will be different, and the difference will be a measure of the inclination (dip) of the horizon. The average of ρ^+ and ρ^- will be the resistivity corresponding to the conventional sounding.

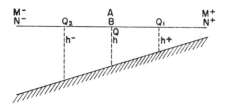

Fig.31. Dipole sounding over inclined bed. h^+ = depth on the up-dip side, h^- = depth on the down-dip side; h = depth (average), is the same as obtained from the symmetrical Schlumberger $AMNB$ arrangement.

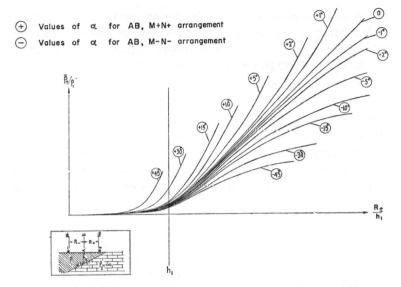

Fig.32. Effect of dip on bilateral equatorial dipole curves. Plus and minus signs for up-dip and down-dip measurements. Second layer resistivity is infinite.

Thus, in case of dipole sounding, we can construct three curves—the positive, the negative and the average resistivity curves.

Let us consider the case of a dipping bed as shown in Fig.31. The conventional sounding $AMNB$ with the centre at O gives the depth of the horizon only at the centre O. If, however, we place at O the current dipole of the bilateral sounding setup, it is possible to get from the three constructed curves, three depths—one on the up-dip side (h^+) at Q_1, one on the down-dip side (h^-) at Q_2 and the average (h) at the centre Q. Thus, the location of the horizon is more reliable for bilateral dipole sounding than the conventional method.

The large number of master curves available for conventional sounding may be used directly for azimuthal (or equatorial) dipole sounding. Special theoretical curves have been constructed for the radial (or axial) dipole sounding of a three-layer earth, and published by ANONYMOUS (1957), along with two sets of two-layer curves.

Theoretical curves are also available for an inclined layer lying on
an insulating or conducting base. Sets of such curves have been
published in English (AL'PIN et al., 1966). Examples of such curves
are shown in Fig.32 (for bilateral equatorial sounding) and Fig.33
(for bilateral axial sounding). It is seen from Fig.32 that even for
an inclination of 2°, the separation between the positive and negative resistivity curves is quite noticeable. For an axial setup, as is
seen from Fig.33, an inclination of as little as 1° can be detected
by the separation of the positive and negative curves. The conventional setup, as mentioned earlier, is insensitive to any inclination less than 15°. Thus, the resolving power of dipole sounding

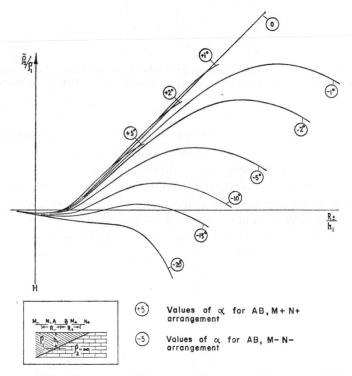

Fig.33. Effect of dip on bilateral axial dipole curves. Plus, minus signs for
up-dip and down-dip measurements. Second layer resistivity is infinite.

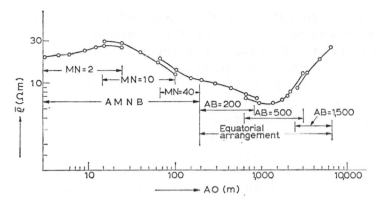

Fig.34. A typical equatorial sounding field curve (after BERDICHEVSKII and PETROVSKII, 1956). Measurements with Schlumberger arrangement up to AO $(= \overline{R})$ 200 m.

is much greater than that of conventional sounding for lateral variations, the axial setup being more sensitive than the equatorial setup.

As the dipole sounding is very sensitive to lateral variations, the inhomogeneities of the surface layers can considerably distort the resistivity values for the deeper layers. This is avoided by using the conventional method for sounding up to a depth of 200–300 m. Beyond that depth the sounding may be undertaken by the dipole method. Fig.34 represents a field curve showing the use of various layouts for different spreads (after BERDICHEVSKII and PETROVSKII, 1956).

In the case of deep sounding by dipole arrangement, the distance between the power and measuring lines is large compared to the lengths of the lines. As a result, the distortion effects due to mutual induction between the lines, and the leakage of current from the power line, are to a great extent reduced. It is claimed that when the length of the power dipole is 1,000–1,500 m, that of the measuring dipole 300–500 m, and the distance between them 10–12 km (for the equatorial position), it is possible to trace the basement at a depth of 2.5–3 km.

Another great advantage of the dipole method is the possibility for sounding on a curved profile. For conventional sounding, the electrodes *AMNB* must lie on a straight line. In difficult areas (e.g., in forest, brush, or swampy areas) it is not always possible to maintain the straight profile for long distances. In view of the fact that dipole sounding (except the parallel setup) is independent of the azimuth, it is not necessary for the centers of all the dipoles to lie on the same straight line. The power dipole may be conveniently located, such that the center of the dipole lies on or near a road. The potential dipole *MN* can be placed at locations on a winding road such that it is in the azimuthal (or radial) position with respect to the power dipole (Fig.35).

At present, most of the deep electric prospecting in the U.S.S.R. is being done by bilateral equatorial (or azimuthal) dipole sounding. As the field due to a dipole decreases as the cube of the distance, the power required for a dipole sounding is larger than that required for a conventional sounding (where the field decreases as the square of the distance). Thus, for deeper investigation, the power required may be of the order of 15–20 kW.

The sounding is usually done by three field stations. The power station for the power dipole remains stationary at one place for a profile. The two measuring stations on either side of the power station move away in steps. Radio communication is maintained between the stations. The length of the power dipole is changed when the intensity of the electric field at the measuring stations

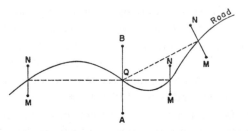

Fig.35. Dipole sounding over a curved path. Potential dipole *MN* in the azimuthal position with respect to the power dipole.

TABLE XIV

A TYPICAL FIELD LAYOUT FOR EQUATORIAL DIPOLE ARRANGEMENT

Observation number [1]	R (m)	$\overline{AB}/2$ (m)	$\overline{MN}/2$ (m)	$\overline{R}$ (m)	K
1	0	3	1	3	1.26
2	0	4.5	1	4.5	3.0
3	0	6	1	6	5.5
4	0	9	1	9	12.6
5	0	12	1	12	22.5
6	0	15	1	15	35.2
7	0	15	5	15	6.2
8	0	25	1	25	98
9	0	25	5	25	18.8
10	0	40	5	40	49.5
11	0	65	5	65	132
12	0	65	20	65	30
13	0	100	5	100	314
14	0	100	20	100	75.5
15	0	150	20	150	174
16	0	200	20	200	311
17	200	200	20	283	8.8
18	400	200	25	447	28.1
19	400	500	25	640	33.1
20	600	200	50	632	40.0
21	800	200	50	825	88.5
22	800	500	50	943	52.9
23	1,200	500	50	1,300	138
24	1,600	500	150	1,676	99.7
25	2,000	500	200	2,061	139
26	2,000	1,500	200	2,500	82.2
27	3,000	500	200	3,041	445
28	3,000	1,500	200	3,340	198
29	4,500	1,500	300	4,743	373
30	6,000	1,500	300	6,184	829
31	8,000	1,500	400	8,139	141.6
32	10,000	1,500	400	10,112	2,713

[1] No. 1–16. The arrangement AMNB : $K = \dfrac{\pi}{10} \dfrac{\left(\dfrac{\overline{AB}}{2}\right)^2 - \left(\dfrac{\overline{MN}}{2}\right)^2}{\overline{MN}}$

(See Fig.2. ΔV in m V; L in A.)

No. 17–32. The equatorial arrangement: $K = \dfrac{\pi}{1,000} \dfrac{\overline{AM} \cdot \overline{AN}}{\overline{AN} - \overline{AM}}$

(See Fig. 30. ΔV in m V; L in A.)

becomes negligible, but always so that length AB is kept less than one-third of R. In planning a field program, it should be kept in mind that for shallower investigations (up to 300–400 m) Schlumberger conventional sounding is taken, and that the value of AB and R should be so chosen that $R(QO)$ is at least three times $L(AB)$—though it can be more. Also, MN should be one-fifth or less of AB. An experimental layout for field work is outlined in Table XIV (BERDICHEVSKII and PETROVSKII, 1956) for equatorial dipole arrangement.

A comparison of Table XIV with Table I clearly indicates that up to a depth of about 20 m, both the Wenner and Schlumberger arrangements are used. After this, up to about 300–400 m, only the Schlumberger arrangement is used; this is followed by dipole sounding for still deeper investigations.

AVAILABLE CURVES AND QUANTITATIVE INTERPRETATION

For azimuthal or equatorial dipole sounding curves (D.E.S.) the method of interpretation is the same as in V.E.S. with $AB/2$ equivalent to $\bar{R}$ (i.e., AO, Fig.30) in D.E.S. R ($= QO$ in Fig.30) is known as "separation" in the equatorial dipole arrangement and $\bar{R}$ ($= AO$ in Fig.30) is the working distance equivalent to $AB/2$ in the Schlumberger vertical electrical sounding. Bilateral D.E.S. curves may be used for determination of a dip angle as low as 5°.

For quantitative interpretation of radial and axial D.E.S. curves, the album of radial master curves published by ANONYMOUS (1957) are available for use. The two-layer master curves for radial arrangement are presented in Plate X.

Theoretical master curves for radial dipole sounding are available for the following three-layer cases:

$$\rho_3/\rho_1 = \infty, \ (\rho_2/\rho_1)^2, \ (\rho_2/\rho_1)^{\frac{3}{2}}, \ (\rho_2/\rho_1)^{\frac{1}{2}}, \ 1, \ 0$$

$$\nu = (h_2/h_1) = 1/9, \ 1/5, \ 1/3, \ 1/2, \ 1, \ 2, \ 3, \ 5, \ 9, \ 24$$

$$\mu = (\rho_2/\rho_1) = 1/39, \ 1/19, \ 1/9, \ 1/4, \ 3/7, \ 2/3, \ 1, \ 3/2, \ 7/3, \ 4, \ 9, \ 19, \ 39, \ \infty$$

TABLE XV

APPARENT RESISTIVITY AND CORRESPONDING HALF-ELECTRODE SEPARATION
(DATA FOR RADIAL DIPOLE FIELD CURVES)

Resistivity (Ωm)

R/2(m):	15	20	30	40	50	60	80	100	150	200	300	400	500	800	1000	1500	2000	3000	4000	5000
D.E.S.																				
1	—	62	61	62	64	68	81	94	120	142	178	200	218	240	240	219	162	50	11.5	—
2	32	32	34	38	44	49	58	65	80	92	108	113	116	110	97	70	48	35	—	—
3	25	24.4	20	16.2	13.3	11.2	8.6	8.2	10	12	14.2	16	18	21	22	23	23	23	23	23
4	7.0	6.8	6.0	5.3	4.7	4.2	4.0	4.4	6.2	8.2	12.2	16.0	20.5	32	42	62	—	—	—	—
5	14.8	15	17	19	22.5	25.5	31	35	42	45	48	54	60	85	103	110	121	134	—	—
6	10	9.8	9.8	10.3	11.0	12.0	14.3	16.3	20.5	24	29.5	34	37	46	50	58	64	73	—	—
7	8.0	7.9	7.8	7.8	7.9	7.4	6.7	6.1	4.6	4.0	3.6	3.1	2.6	0.8	0.3	—	—	—	—	—
8	300	300	295	295	290	280	240	200	134	100	80	74	72	70	67	59	50	43	40	38

The curves are plotted on double-logarithm scale (with a modulus of 62.5 mm), with $\bar{\rho}/\rho_1$ along the ordinate, and $R/2h_1$ along the abscissa. Out of the 62 sets of curves 2 are for two-layer cases. In this case, R is the distance between the current and the measuring dipoles.

The interpretation procedure for three-layer radial dipole sounding field curves with the help of published curves (ANONYMOUS, 1957) may be summarized as follows:

(*a*) Superpose the left-hand part of the three-layer D.E.S. field curve over the two-layer master curve set (for radial, Plate X). Keep the axes parallel, and try to obtain a match with one of the two-layer curves. This gives ρ_1, h_1 and $\mu = \rho_2/\rho_1$. In case, there is no match, use interpolation.

(*b*) Try to guess at a value of ρ_3 from the asymptotic part of the curve, and note the approximate value of ρ_3/ρ_1.

(*c*) Try to match the curve now, as a whole, over any of the three-layer curves available. An approximate value for ρ_3/ρ_1 acts as a guide in the choice of the proper set of three-layer master curves. If an exact match is obtained, this gives the value of $\mu = \rho_2/\rho_1$ and $\nu = h_2/h_1$ as well as the value of ρ_3.

(*d*) Repeat step (*c*) in order to get a refined set of values if an exact match has not already been obtained in step (*c*).

PROBLEM

Plot the three-layer radial D.E.S. field curves from the values given in Table XV and then interpret the curves with the help of the two-layer (Plate X) and the available three-layer master curves (ANONYMOUS, 1957) for radial arrangement. Use a graph sheet with a modulus equal to 62.5 mm.

CHAPTER 6

Geological Applications

Geological information regarding the formations which constitute surface and subsurface lithology is a necessity in the correct interpretation of geoelectric sounding data. Further, drillhole data at selected points are needed both for control and confirmation of the results of geological investigations. From the point of view of geophysical prospecting, an important prerequisite is knowledge of the strike and the dip of formations; these must be known at least roughly. For horizontally stratified earth, there is no problem in the choice of the profile for sounding. In the case of dipping beds, the sounding line is laid parallel to the known or estimated strike of the formations. Therefore, the strike should be known geologically, at least approximately, and confirmed geophysically by taking two soundings at right angles to each other. As already noted in Chapter 5, a dip of up to 15° does not affect the nature of V.E.S. curves appreciably, but D.E.S. curves reflect the effect of a dip as low as 2–3°.

Electrical resistivity sounding, as applied to various geological problems, will be discussed briefly in the next few sections.

ENGINEERING PROBLEMS

Vertical electrical sounding, both Schlumberger and Wenner, can be utilized for shallow engineering (civil and military) investigations, such as the testing of foundations for the construction of highways, railroads, bridges, dams, canals, reservoir sites, field fortifications, shelters, munition plants, or for the location of construction material. The problems mentioned here reduce to two main types: (*1*) determination of thickness of the overburden, or depth to the bedrock; (*2*) location of construction material.

The base of the weathered zone presents a good resistivity contrast (highly resistive basement), representing a two-layer case; with the second layer resistivity very high, the interpretation becomes very simple and quick (Chapter 3). All engineering structures need to be built with the foundation within solid rock.

In the construction of tunnels, after locating the thrust zone (if there be any), the condition of subsurface water may be studied by sounding. This is possible because the crushed and water-saturated zone usually shows a low resistivity. The results of sounding may lead to a change in the direction and design of the tunnel. The same is also true for mine shafts. Sounding can also be used in the location of construction material when covered with alluvium.

In such engineering problems, vertical electrical sounding (preferably with Wenner configuration) is recommended, since the problems are related to shallow investigations only. However, the Schlumberger configuration, with a smaller spread length, can also be used.

ORE PROSPECTING AND HYDROGEOLOGICAL PROBLEMS

Ore prospecting

In ore prospecting, sounding has a limited application. Determining the exact location of deposits is possible when the ore deposits are bedded ones, as, for example, in the case of coal. It is also possible to locate certain minerals indirectly by mapping the associated structures and zones of unconformity.

Resistivity sounding can be used to locate placer deposits of gold, platinum, diamonds, etc. The main task of sounding here is to map the underground relief and to determine the thickness of the friable sediments. Even in the case of geophysical investigation by profiling, a preliminary sounding must be done in the initial stages to fix the current electrode separation to be used for profiling.

In general, in ore prospecting, sounding is widely used primarily for the determination of the thickness of the quaternary sediments.

Hydrogeological problems

There are many applications of geophysics in water-supply and -control problems. Control includes the design and construction of irrigation and drainage projects, such as canals and aqueducts, and in the planning of dam and reservoir sites for flood control and power projects. This part of the problem has already been discussed in Chapter 5, under engineering problems.

Prospecting for water is essentially a geological problem, and the geophysical approach is dependent on the mode of the geological occurrence of water. Water may occur as: (*1*) ground water proper; (*2*) fissure water; (*3*) mineral springs; (*4*) cavern water; and (*5*) water issuing out of leaks, etc.

Geophysically, the location of ground water may be determined in three ways: (*1*) direct; (*2*) stratigraphic, and (*3*) structural.

Direct methods are largely confined to well-logging, or locating the sites of radioactive and thermal springs. The stratigraphic method implies locating water-bearing formations through distinguishing physical properties imparted by the presence of water, such as high seismic velocity, or increased or decreased electrical conductivity. The structural approach means the mapping of key beds that bear a certain stratigraphic or structural relation to the water-bearing bed, i.e., mapping of synclines, erosional troughs, or structural lows. Where erosional troughs or structural depressions are formed by igneous or metamorphic rocks related to basement topography, the magnetic method is suitable. When bedrock is nonmagnetic, and differs in density, the bedrock may be mapped by a gravity survey.

Most problems involving bedrock depth determination are best handled by seismic and electrical resistivity methods. Exceptional cases, such as large-scale artesian basins of considerable depth, can be mapped by D.E.S. or by the seismic reflection method.

In arid zones, geophysical prospecting for ground water can be done by means of electromagnetic sounding, where resistivity surveys cannot be conducted because the surface rocks have high resistivity.

In the stratigraphic method of location, use is made of the fact that water-bearing strata often differ in elasticity or electrical conductivity from other formations in a series. Seismic refraction has been used for locating the ground-water table. Unconsolidated sediments, when saturated with water, show a considerable increase in seismic velocity. A similar velocity contrast, which occurs at the base of weathered zones, is applied to engineering problems. Usually, however, geophysical prospecting for ground water is done by the electrical resistivity method, at comparatively low cost.

Thus, it is seen from the above discussion that vertical electrical sounding (V.E.S.) is the most suitable method for ground-water investigation in most geological occurrences. V.E.S. with the Schlumberger (preferably) configuration is recommended for geophysical exploration of ground water. The Wenner sounding may be used for shallow occurrences, such as the water-saturated zone at the base of a weathered layer. Dipole electric sounding (D.E.S.) may be used in exceptional cases, such as large scale artesian basins of sufficient depth.

Examples of actual field problems on the stratigraphic location of water are given at the end of this chapter.

STRUCTURAL MAPPING FOR OIL

Vertical electrical sounding with Schlumberger configuration may be used for the determination of shallow structure, buried anticlines, etc., for oil exploration, provided the structures are at a comparatively shallow depth.

Dipole electric sounding (D.E.S.) can, however, be applied for regional investigations of large, unexplored territories and for prospecting local, deeper structures interesting from the point of view of possible oil and gas accumulation. D.E.S. can give knowledge of regional characteristics which may help in locating structures underlying very thick sediments of uniform and thick geoelectrical section, suitable for oil accumulation.

EXAMPLES

Example 1

Fig.36 gives the results of vertical electrical sounding with Schlumberger configuration only, for the location of groundwater in some coastal regions by the stratigraphic approach. This

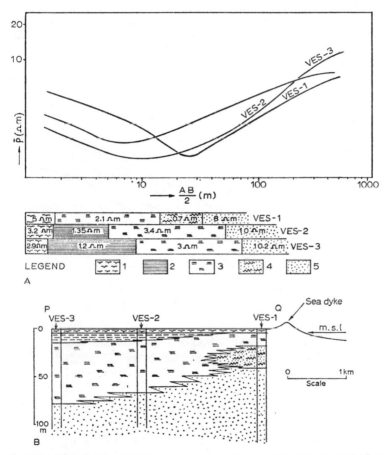

Fig.36A. Schlumberger V.E.S. curves representing section *PQ*. B. Geological section along *PQ* prepared from the information given in A. Key: *1* = alluvium (3–5 Ωm); *2* = plastic clay (1–2 Ωm); *3* = silt and sand (3–4 Ωm); *4* = salt water bearing fine sand (< 1 Ωm); *5* = medium clay sand (8–12 Ωm).

refers to the investigations in connection with the possibility of saline water invasion (PATRA, 1967). Fig.36A gives the field curves at three selected stations on a line, while the probable geological section obtained from interpretation of the curves is presented in Fig.36B.

Example 2

Fig.37 gives an illustration of an investigation similar to example 1 —i.e., a hydrogeological problem. Fig.37A contains the sounding

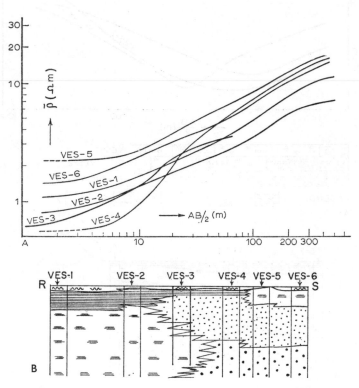

Fig.37A. Schlumberger V.E.S. curves representing section *RS*. Key same as in Fig.36A; resistivity more than 15 Ωm for medium to coarse sand. B. Geological section along *RS* prepared from the information obtained with the curves presented in Fig.37A.

TABLE XVI

APPARENT RESISTIVITY AND CORRESPONDING HALF-ELECTRODE SEPARATION
(SCHLUMBERGER SOUNDING DATA FOR GEOLOGICAL INTERPRETATION)

V.E.S.		AB/2 (m): 2	3	4	5	6	8	10	15	20	30	40	50	80	100	150	200	250	300	400	500
Set I	1	33	30	27	24	22	16	11.7	5.9	4.0	3.4	4.0	4.5	6.4	7.1	8.4	9.7	10.8	11.4	12.8	—
	2	4.75	6.5	8.85	11	13	17.1	19.6	16.4	12.8	8.6	6.2	5.6	7.7	9.6	13.3	15	16	17.5	18	19.5
	3	42	37	34.2	31	26.8	23.2	15.4	8.65	5.92	4.84	5.1	5.95	8.1	9.75	12.5	14.9	16.4	16.8	18	19
Set II	1	1.44	1.50	1.65	1.84	2.05	2.34	2.58	2.94	3.20	3.62	4.06	4.60	5.80	7.05	9.5	11.4	12.2	12.8	13.7	14.9
	2	4.75	6.5	8.85	11	13	17.1	19.6	16.4	12.8	8.6	6.2	5.6	7.7	9.6	13.3	15	16	17.5	18	19.5
	3	3.3	2.65	2.4	2.2	2.1	2.35	2.48	2.75	3.2	4.2	4.7	5.2	6.8	6.1	7.9	11.2	12.4	13.6	15	16
	4	2.05	1.9	1.9	1.7	1.8	1.95	2.0	2.15	2.42	2.9	3.4	3.95	5.2	6.1	7.8	10	11.4	12	14	16
	5	3.85	3.3	2.75	2.55	2.40	2.35	2.44	2.50	2.55	2.84	3.3	3.8	5.0	5.95	7.55	9.1	10	11.5	13	14

Resistivity (Ωm)

curves along a line, and Fig.37B represents the geological section prepared from the interpreted results in connection with exploration for ground water (PATRA and BHATTACHARYA, 1966).

PROBLEMS

Problem 1

Interpret the set of V.E.S. field curves plotted from the values given in Table XVI (Set I) obtained for the Schlumberger electrode arrangement, and prepare a geological section from the interpreted results. Assume that the sounding stations, serially located, are along a straight line—with a station spacing equal to 1 km, and the total length of the line = 2 km. The field work is supposed to be carried out in a sedimentary area. Alternating beds of sand and clay, covered with a thin layer of alluvium, are expected to exist (evident from available borehole data).

Problem 2

Interpret the given set of Schlumberger V.E.S. field curves, plotted from the values presented in Table XVI (Set II), with the positions of the sounding stations, serially arranged, along a straight line. The station spacing is equal to 0.5 km, and the total length of the line = 2 km. The geological conditions are found to be the same as in problem 1.

References

AL'PIN, L. M., 1940. Ne gorizontalnye poverkhhnosti razdelai paletki. *Prikl. Geofiz., Vses. Nauchn. Issled. Inst. Geofiz. Metodov Razvedki, Sb. Statei*, 1.

AL'PIN, L. M., 1950. *Teoriya Dipolnykh Zondirovanii*. Gostoptekhizdat, Moskva, 91 pp.

AL'PIN, L. M., BERDICHEVKSII, M. N., VEDRINTSEV, G. A. and ZAGARMISTR, A. M., 1966. *Dipole Methods for Measuring Earth Conductivity*. Consultants Bur., New York, N.Y., 302 pp.

ANONYMOUS—VSES. NAUCHN. ISSLED. INST. GEOFIZ., 1957. *Paletki, Teoreticheskikh Krivikh Radialnogo Dipolnago Zondirovanya*. Gosgeoltekhizdat, Moskva, 62 pp. (master curves).

ANONYMOUS—VSES. NAUCHN. ISSLED. INST. GEOFIZ., 1963a. *Al'bom Paletok Electricheskogo Zondirovanya dlya Trekhsloinykh Gorizontal'no–Odnorodnykh Razrezov*. Gosgeoltekhizdat, Moskva, 120 pp. (master curves).

ANONYMOUS—VSES. NAUCHN. ISSLED. INST. GEOFIZ., 1963b. *Al'bom Paletok, Elektricheskogo Zondirovanya dlya Chetirekhsloinykh Gorizontal'no–Odnorodnykh Razrezov*. Moskva, 120 pp. (master curves).

ANONYMOUS—VSES. NAUCHN. ISSLED. INST. GEOFIZ., 1963c. *Al'bom Paletok, Electricheskogo Zondirovanya dlya Razrezov s Verticalnymi, Naklonnymi i Gorizontal'no–Vertikalnymi Kontaktami*. Gosgeoltekhizdat, Moskva, 120 pp. (master curves).

BELLUIGI, A., 1956. Berechnung der elektrischen Leitfähigkeit des Oberflächenpotentials. *Beitr. Geophys.*, 65 (3): 171–184.

BERDICHEVSKII, M. N. and PETROVSKII, A. D., 1956. Metodika vypolneniya dvustoronnikh ekvatorial'nykh zondirovanii. *Prikl. Geofiz., Vses. Nauchn. Issled. Inst. Geofiz. Metodov Razvedki, Sb. Statei*, 14: 97–114.

COMPAGNIE GÉNÉRALE DE GÉOPHYSIQUE, 1955. Abaque de sondage électrique. *Geophys. Prospecting*, 3 (Suppl.3): 50 pp.

COMPAGNIE GÉNÉRALE DE GÉOPHYSIQUE, 1963. *Master Curves for Electrical Sounding*, 2nd Ed. European Assoc. Exploration Geophysicists, The Hague, 49 pp.

DAKHNOV, V. N., 1953. *Electricheskaya Rajvedka*. Gostoptekhizdat, Moskva, 497 pp.

DE GERY, J. C. and KUNETZ, G., 1956. Potential and apparent resistivity over dipping beds. *Geophysics*, 21: 780–793.

DEPPERMANN, K., 1954. Die Abhängigkeit des scheinbaren Widerstandes vom Sondenabstand bei der Vierpunkt-Methode. *Geophys. Prospecting*, 2 (4): 262–273.

DOBRIN, M. B., 1960. *Introduction to Geophysical Prospecting.* McGraw-Hill, New York, N.Y., 446 pp.

EBERT, A., 1943. Grundlagen zur Auswertung geoelektrischer Tiefenmessungen. *Beitr. Angew. Geophys.*, 10: 1–17.

FLATHE, H., 1955. A practical method of calculating geoelectrical model graphs for horizontally stratified media. *Geophys. Prospecting*, 3: 268–294.

HEILAND, C. A., 1942. Geophysics in war. *Quart. Colo. School Mines*, 37 (1): 85.

KALENOV, E. N., 1957. *Interpretatsia Krivikh Verticalnogo Electrichekogo Zondirovanya.* Gostoptekhizdat, Moskva, 470 pp.

KELLER, G. V. and FRISCHKNECHT, F. C., 1967. *Electrical Methods in Geophysical Prospecting.* Pergamon, New York, N.Y., 519 pp.

KELLY, S. F., 1962. Geophysical exploration for water by electrical resistivity. *J. New Engl. Water Works Assoc.*, 76 (2): 168.

KOEFOED, O., 1965. A semi-direct method of interpreting resistivity observations. *Geophys. Prospecting*, 13 (2): 259–282.

KUNETZ, G., 1966. *Principles of Direct Current Resistivity Prospecting.* Bornträger, Berlin, 106 pp.

LASFARGUES, P., 1957. *Prospection Électrique.* Masson, Paris, 290 pp.

MAEDA, K., 1955. Apparent resistivity for dipping beds. *Geophysics*, 20 (1): 123–139.

MAILLET, R., 1947. The fundamental equations of electrical prospecting. *Geophysics*, 12 (4): 529–556.

MOONEY, H. M., 1954. Depth determination by electrical resistivity. *Mining Engr.*, 6 (9): 915–918.

MOONEY, H. M. and WETZEL, W. W., 1956. *The Potentials about a Point Electrode and Apparent Resistivity Curves for a Two-, Three- and Four-Layer Earth.* Univ. Minnesota, Minneapolis, Minn., 146 pp.

MOONEY, H. M., ORELLANA, E., PICKETT, H. and TORNHEIM, L., 1966. A resistivityc omputation method for layered earth models. *Geophysics*, 31 (1): 192–203.

ORELLANA, E. and MOONEY, H. M., 1966. *Master Tables and Curves for Vertical Electrical Sounding over Layered Structures.* Interciencia, Madrid, 193 pp.

PATRA, H. P., 1967. On the possibility of saline water invasion around the Jaldha coast, West Bengal (India). *Geoexploration*, 5 (2): 95–101.

PATRA, H. P. and BHATTACHARYA, P. K., 1966. Geophysical exploration for ground water around Digha in the coastal region of West-Bengal, India. *Geoexploration*, 4 (4): 209–218.

PYLAEV, A. M., 1948. *Rykovodstvo po Interpretatsi Vertikal'nykh Electricheskikh Zondirovanii.* Gosgeolizdat, Moskva, 168 pp.

RI, SOK-HANG, 1961. Das Gleichstromdipolverfahren für geoelektrische Prospektion. *Freiberger Forschungsh.*, C114: 98 pp.

SLICHTER, L. B., 1933. The interpretation of resitivity prospecting method for horizontal structures. *Physics*, 8: 307–322.

TAGG, G. F., 1964. *Earth Resistance.* George Newnes Ltd., London, 258 pp.

TARKHOV, A. G., 1963. *Spravochnik Geofizika. 3. Electrorazvedka.* Gostoptekhizdat, Moskva, 482 pp.

TIKHONOV, A. N., 1946. Ob electro-zondirovanii nadnaklonnym plastom. *Tr. Inst. Teor. Geofiz., Akad. Nauk S.S.S.R.*, 1: 116–136.

UNZ, M., 1953. Apparent resistivity curves tor dipping beds. *Geophysics*, 18: 116–137.

VAN DAM, J. C., 1965. A simple method for calculation of standard-graphs to be used in geoelectrical prospecting. *Geophys. Prospecting*, 13 (1): 37–64.

VAN DAM, J. C., 1967. Mathematical denotation of standard-graphs for resistivity prospecting in view of their calculation by means of a digital computer. *Geophys. Prospecting*, 15 (1): 57–70.

VAN NOSTRAND, R. G. and COOK, K. L., 1966. Interpretation of resisitivity data. *U.S. Geol. Surv., Prof. Papers*, 499: 310 pp.

ZABOROVOSKII, A. I., 1963. *Electrorazvedka*. Gostoptekhizdat, Moskva, 423 pp.

ZOHDY, A. A. R., 1965. The auxiliary point method of electrical sounding interpretation and its relationship to the Dar Zarrouk parameters. *Geophysics*, 30 (4): 644–660.

Index